KEYS TO HEALTH
WHOLENESS
& FRUITFULNESS

STEVE GOSS & DR MARY WREN

AN 8-SESSION ADVENTURE TO HELP YOU
LIVE WELL IN SPIRIT, MIND, AND BODY

Keys To Health, Wholeness, & Fruitfulness

Participant's Guide

American English Version

Copyright © Freedom In Christ Ministries International 2019.

Published and printed by Freedom In Christ Ministries International
4 Beacontree Plaza, Gillette Way, Reading RG2 0BS, UK.

ISBN 978-1-913082-08-6

First edition 2019

Comments From Participants

"This course has been amazing for me and has given me practical tools to use."

"Knowing who I am in Christ has absolutely set me free!"

"It helps to deal with the root cause of issues rather than just dealing with the surface symptoms."

"It's given me a much deeper understanding of the connection between the Biblical, scientific, and medical aspects of health, wholeness, and fruitfulness."

"Over the last few years I've struggled with anxiety and depression. It's become part of my identity. But what I've realized through doing this course is that it's not my identity at all."

"A true understanding of wholeness came through in both the medical and the spiritual sense."

"It has given me such freedom to realize that my identity is not tied to any disease and I don't have to 'own' it."

"I've had some issues about feeling worthless because of what people have said in my past. I looked at the scriptures and found out who I really am in Christ. That's just really transformed me!"

"This course has made me realize how God heals not only spiritually but through my doctor as well."

"We're surrounded by 'good advice' about health and you never really know what to believe. A true understanding of wholeness came through from both the medical and the spiritual sense."

A Radical Step

Steve Goss, our International Director, explains why we've made the video presentations for *Keys To Health, Wholeness, & Fruitfulness* completely free:

"Our great passion is to equip the Church to transform the nations. Our call is to produce discipleship resources that church leaders can use to help every Christian across every generation become a fruitful disciple who makes a real difference.

A resource such as this one typically takes over five years to write, test, refine, and produce. The final product seems so precious to us that, when we film the accompanying video material, we want it to be the very best, so we use top-quality Christian film-makers and state-of-the-art production facilities.

That doesn't come cheap and we usually try to recoup our costs and raise money for future resources by selling the videos. But we are well aware that our calling is to equip the Church to make fruitful disciples who will transform the nations, not to be a publishing business. So with this resource, we're taking a radical step and making the video available for free in the hope that it will spread far and wide and make a much greater impact. We're trusting that God will give us a new model to fund future resources. It's an exciting step!"

Find out how to access the videos on page 7. Interested in joining with us to produce further top-quality discipleship resources, or to translate existing ones into other languages? Find out how you can help on page 195.

Important Note For Participants

Some Christians have been taught that seeking medical help is somehow "unspiritual" or demonstrates a lack of faith in God. It is neither of those things, but is an eminently sensible course of action. Medical professionals are part of God's provision for our health.

This course is not an alternative to consulting a medical doctor. If you have a health issue that needs treatment or investigation, and you have not already done so, do not delay in seeking medical advice.

CONTENTS

FREEDOM IN CHRIST

Get More Out Of The Course

Steve Goss has written four slim, easy-to-digest books that present Freedom In Christ's discipleship teaching. They are published by Monarch and are available from Freedom In Christ Ministries (see FreedomInChrist. org for your nearest office) and other booksellers.

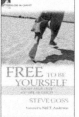

Free to be Yourself – Enjoy your true nature in Christ.
Many Christians act as they think a Christian should act – and find that they simply can't keep it up. They either drop out or burn out. True fruitfulness comes from realizing that we became someone completely new the moment we became Christians.

Win the Daily Battle – Resist and stand firm.
You are in a raging battle, whether you like it or not. Your only choice is to stand and fight or to become a casualty. Arrayed against you are the world, the devil and the flesh but once you understand how they work and just who you are in Christ, you can expect to emerge victorious from every skirmish with them.

Break Free, Stay Free – Don't let the past hold you back.
Every Christian has a past. It can hold us back big-time. Those of us with a lot of "stuff" know that only too well. But even those who have had a relatively trouble-free existence need to know how to resolve negative influences that stop us moving on.

The You God Planned – Don't let anything hold you back!
Once we have claimed our freedom in Christ, how do we remain in it and make fruitfulness a way of life? How do we know what God is calling us to be anyway? Are the goals we have for our lives in line with His goals? How can we stop others getting in the way? And how do we avoid getting in their way?

GET STARTED

Keys To Health, Wholeness, & Fruitfulness is designed primarily as a study for small groups running under the guidance of a local church but you can also go through it on your own. For small groups it works best if someone is appointed to lead each session.

1. ACCESS THE FREE VIDEO PRESENTATIONS

In order to get started, you need to access the video presentations for each session. Beause we believe passionately that the Church needs this message, we are making them available free of charge. To find out how to see them, go to:

www.FreedomInChrist.org/health

2. GO THROUGH THE SESSIONS

There are eight main sessions, two optional sessions, a ministry component called *The Steps To Healing And Wholeness*, and a bonus video for participants who want to look in a little more depth at the question of addiction.

Start each session by considering the **Welcome** question, and taking part in the **Worship** time (we have suggested themes for this). Then move to the **Word** section which contains the teaching and discussion times. Start by watching the video for that session. When you reach the first Pause For Thought discussion time, pause the video (the "Pause" symbol will appear on the screen). After your discussion, continue with the second part of the video until you come to the second Pause For Thought discussion time. This is followed by a short conclusion which includes seven "Keys To Take Home", a summary of what has been covered that you can consider during the coming week (there's one for each day).

Every participant will need their own copy of this Participant's Guide.

3. DON'T MISS *THE STEPS TO HEALING AND WHOLENESS*

The Steps To Healing And Wholeness is different from the other sessions. It is a self-explanatory ministry component designed to be run in your group on an additional "away day" together or as a one-on-one process. It comes after Session 8 and we strongly advise groups to get a date on the calendar for this as soon as you begin to run the course from the very first session. It is an essential part of the course and it would be a great shame for any participant to miss it.

The Freedom In Christ App

This app was written for participants on our best-selling *Freedom In Christ Course* but it is extremely useful for those going through Keys To Health, Wholeness, & Fruitfulness too, particularly the "Stronghold-Buster-Builder".

- Get a daily nugget of truth tailored to where you are on the course delivered to your device.
- Access key lists of Biblical truths.
- Extra teaching films on key topics.
- Powerful Stronghold-Buster-Builder tool: find your Bible verses, create your Stronghold-Buster, and specify when you wish to be reminded to use it.
- Sample songs from *Worship In Spirit And Truth*, the album written to accompany the course, and see films of the songwriters, Wayne and Esther Tester and Nicole C. Mullen, sharing why Freedom In Christ is so important to them personally.
- Get a daily devotional from Neil Anderson, Founder of Freedom In Christ, delivered to your device.

Search for "Freedom In Christ" in your app store. In case of difficulty, go to **FreedomInChrist.org/app** where you will find the app store links.

Transforming Health

WHAT'S IT ABOUT?

This is an optional session that serves as a gentle introduction to the main sessions. It is about half as long as a standard session.

OBJECTIVE:

To introduce the course and the presenters of the videos.

WELCOME

Do you think a Christian should expect to be in better health than someone who has not yet taken the step to make Jesus their Lord? Why? / Why not?

WORSHIP

Praise God for the transformation you have seen Him bring in and through His people:

- We are "the light of the world" (Matthew 5:14);
- God intends us to shine like stars in a "warped and crooked generation." (Philippians 2:14).

Video length: 20:44.

WORD

Watch the video and then discuss the Pause For Thought questions.

Meet The Presenters

Dr. Mary Wren is the main inspiration for Keys To Health, Wholeness, & Fruitfulness. She wanted to be a doctor from the age of 10 and studied medicine in Sheffield in the North of England. While she was a student, she had a series of illnesses during which she started to learn how to seek God for help and wisdom as well as seeking medical help. For each new situation she has sought God for "keys" to unlock the answers. She works at Sheffield University Health Service as one of the doctors for 35,000 university students. She wrote a weekly column for a newspaper and loves the detective work of medicine – getting to the root of the problem be it physical, emotional, or spiritual – and sees herself as a bridge between medicine and the Church.

Steve Goss passionately believes that a community of committed, fruitful disciples of Jesus can transform a nation. He and his wife Zoë founded Freedom In Christ's UK office in 1999. They now head up Freedom In Christ globally and are constantly amazed to see God opening doors all around the world. Freedom In Christ now works in around 40 countries. Steve co-wrote *The Freedom In Christ Course* that has been used by around 500,000 people as well as many other resources.

Dr. Ifeoma Monye has a passion for preventing, treating, and, if possible, reversing the course of chronic diseases using the principles of "Lifestyle Medicine". She has a passion to share how we can make simple lifestyle choices every day to live healthier and happier to pursue our purpose and fulfill our destiny. She divides her time between Nigeria and the UK. In Abuja, she is a Chief Consultant Family Physician at the National Hospital and founder of the Brookfield Center For Lifestyle Medicine. She is the founding President of the African Lifestyle Medicine Association. In the UK, she works as a family doctor. Ifeoma is married with four children and enjoys serving in the intercessory group at her church.

Meet The Rest Of The Team

Keys To Health, Wholeness, And Fruitfulness was developed over a period of five years. During most of that time, the content was worked on by Steve Goss together with a team of medical professionals: Dr. Mary Wren; Lorna Nicholson; Dr. Sue Sorensen; and Dr. Alison Fleetwood. They were joined in the later stages by two more professionals, Dr. Ifeoma Monye, and Judith King. You can read about Steve, Mary, and Ifeoma on the preceding pages. Meet the rest of the team here!

Dr. Sue Sorensen is the daughter of an Anglican vicar. She wanted to be a doctor from an early age and now works as a family doctor in the North of England. She has spent time working as a doctor in the Philippines and Nepal, and some time at Bible College. Sue has a particular passion to help those struggling with hurts, hang-ups and habits, and runs groups in her church. You can see Sue sharing her experience in the bonus session, *Freedom From Addiction*.

Dr. Alison Fleetwood works as a family doctor in England's Lake District. She is involved in healing ministries and is a Lay Canon in the Church of England. Alison loves the opportunity to work in the area of healing both in the medical sphere and in the Christian sphere. Alison is married with a teenage son, and in her spare time enjoys walking, cats, and coffee with friends. You can see her tell something of her story in Session 1 of the course.

Lorna Nicholson spends half her time working as an Advanced Nurse Practitioner in a doctor's surgery pratice. In the other half of her time she teaches Pilates, and is especially keen to use it to help those with chronic conditions. Before this, she spent many years working in hospital acute care units. In 2006 Lorna became unwell with an unexplained very rapid heart rate, which, after a number of years, was diagnosed as Postural Tachycardia Syndrome (POTS). Though she has not yet been healed and needs medication to control symptoms, Lorna regards herself as more whole than she was before becoming unwell. She has learned to improve symptoms through lifestyle changes, such as improving sleep, stress reduction, dietary changes, and ensuring adequate exercise, overall doing life at a slower pace. She tells her story in Session 8 of the course.

Judith King is a clinical therapist with 38 years of experience. She integrates biblical and psychological principles and has a particular interest in caring for people in leadership; caregivers, and professionals in ministry as well as in women's issues of all dimensions. She works in private practice, SonLife Associates, which she co-founded with her late husband, Dr. Stephen King, who was a psychiatrist. She serves on the Boards of Freedom In Christ USA and Freedom In Christ International and lives in Grand Rapids, Michigan, USA.

Created For A Purpose

 WHAT'S IT ABOUT?

OBJECTIVE:

To understand that:

- Good physical health is not an end in itself but a means to help us be and do all that God intends for us as fruitful disciples of Jesus.
- Our natural worldview predisposes us to see reality in a way that does not line up with how God says it actually is, so we need to make a constant effort to see things as they really are.
- Jesus died so that we might be healthy, whole, and fruitful but there is a question of timing.
- A complete answer comes only if we look at the whole person – spirit, mind, and body.
- Lasting healing comes by uncovering the root cause of a particular issue and resolving it.

FOCUS VERSE: For we are God's handiwork, created in Christ Jesus to do good works, which God prepared in advance for us to do. (Ephesians 2:10)

 WELCOME

If you were given the opportunity to ask God one question about health, wholeness, and fruitfulness as a disciple of Jesus, what would you ask Him?

WORSHIP

Praise God for His creation:

- Everything that ever existed was created through Jesus and for Jesus (Colossians 1:16);
- His creation is "very good" (Genesis 1:31);
- Each one of us was "fearfully and wonderfully made" (Psalm 139:14).

Video length: 35:31

Pause For Thought 1 comes in at 20:04.

Pause For Thought 2 comes in at 32:47.

WORD

Confused?

The internet has brought a huge array of dubious cures written in pseudo-scientific language. Sometimes legitimate science doesn't seem much better. What experts tell us is good or bad for us seems to change with alarming regularity. Then there's the Church.... There's a lot about wholeness and healing in the Bible, but different people say different things about what it means in practice.

We're going to try to come up with some reliable answers.

What Does It Mean To Be Healthy?

The World Health Organization said that health is "a state of complete physical, mental, and social well-being and not merely the absence of disease or infirmity."

The Bible adds a further crucial dimension: spiritual well-being.

Good physical health is not our end goal on this course. We want to help you work out how to be the person God created you to be, spirit, mind, and body, so that you can do the things that God says He has prepared specifically for you to do.

Adopt A Biblical Worldview

All of us have learned to see reality in a particular way, and differently to how God tells us it actually is.

Our worldview has been shaped by our culture, our education, our families, our friends, the media we consume.

In Africa, for example, most people grow up with the belief that our lives are controlled by a kind of universal power that runs through everything – animals, plants, minerals – and by spirits of many types. So when you fall ill, you are likely to assume that an enemy may be afflicting you with this illness by manipulating the universal power or the spirits against you. Traditionally, in order to sort it out, you would turn not to a medical doctor but to a shaman or witch doctor, someone who you believe knows how to deal with this universal power and the spirits.

The most widespread outbreak of Ebola took place in West Africa between 2013 and 2016. Over 11,000 people died. A significant factor in the spread of the virus is that people trusted their animistic worldview more than they trusted Western medicine. They refused to have their relatives quarantined, preferring instead to take them to a witch doctor. People died as a result.

In the West most of us have learned to look at reality in a scientific, physical way as though it is simply what you can see, touch, and test. A medical text book will teach that you are simply a collection of atoms and molecules and chemicals and doesn't talk about the spirit at all. So if we have a serious illness we would tend to go straight to a medical doctor with the belief that we need tests done and then physical treatments such as a pill or an operation. But up to half of the symptoms reported to doctors appear not to have any physical cause[1].

In no way do we want to deny the amazing truths that science has uncovered and continues to uncover, but what science teaches as fact today, might turn out not to be fact tomorrow, when new discoveries bring a different perspective.

---

1 http://bjgp.org/content/63/617/625

The Bible Shows Us What The World Is Really Like

The principles in the Bible, however, are timeless and we need to give the Bible a higher place. It is God's message to the people He created and it alone reveals what reality is actually like. (If you want to explore that a little more there's an extra video here: www.FreedomInChrist.org/health.)

PAUSE FOR THOUGHT 1

How does the way you learned to look at the world affect the way you have tended to view health and wholeness? In what ways does the Bible bring a different emphasis or perspective?

The Original Design – Body, Mind, And Spirit

One of the key facts we learn from the Bible is that God created our ancient ancestors, whom it calls Adam and Eve. Christians have different views on exactly how He did that. Some have no problem believing in a literal seven-day creation while others think He did it a different way over a long time. Science confirms that we are all descended from one man and one woman – the evidence is in our Y chromosomes and mitochondrial DNA.

When God created them, He gave them a physical body. But they were much more than that. God created them in His own image (Genesis 1:26) and, as God is spirit (John 4:24), we too, at the deepest level, are spiritual beings.

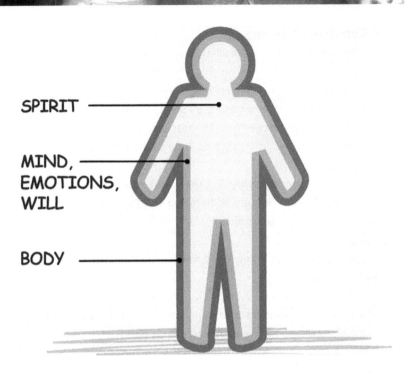

SPIRIT

MIND,
EMOTIONS,
WILL

BODY

It can be helpful to picture ourselves in three layers: at the center we are spirit. On the outside we have our physical body. Linking the two are our mind, emotions, and will.

Western medicine focuses primarily on the body. It considers the mind and emotions to some extent, but generally ignores the spirit altogether.

To have a true understanding of health, wholeness, and fruitfulness, we need to consider our whole person.

A Question Of Timing

The Bible talks of two eras in which everyone is in perfect health.

The first was back when God created the world and declared His creation "very good" (Genesis 1:31). Adam and Eve's spirits were alive and connected to God. They had perfect bodies with no sickness and they didn't experience any negative mental or emotional issues such as anxiety or depression.

When Adam chose to disobey God, there were significant consequences for him and for us. His spirit was cut off from God, and he handed his right to rule the world over to Satan, God's enemy.

One way or another, all illness and disease – spirit, mind, and body – can be traced back to that point.

Which is why God sent Jesus, His only son, to die in our place. Here is a prophecy about Him written many years before He was born:

> Surely he took up our pain [or griefs]
>
> and bore our suffering [or sorrows],
>
> yet we considered him punished by God,
>
> stricken by him, and afflicted.
>
> But he was pierced for our transgressions,
>
> he was crushed for our iniquities;
>
> the punishment that brought us peace was on him,
>
> and by his wounds we are healed.
>
> (Isaiah 53:4-5)

We can say both "griefs and sorrows" and "pain and suffering" – the original words carry both meanings.

Jesus came to deal with our sin, our physical infirmities, and our mental torment. "By his wounds we are healed."

Over a hundred times in the New Testament we find the Greek word, *sozo*. It is usually translated "salvation" but it also carries the sense of "healing," "deliverance," "freedom," and "wholeness".

Jesus came to destroy all the works of the evil one, which include sickness, disease and death. He died and rose again so that we could be whole in spirit, mind, and body.

The second era when followers of Jesus will be perfectly healthy is in the future when Jesus will return. There will be a new heaven and earth, no more suffering, and we will have healthy new bodies that live for ever.

Right now we live between those eras, after Jesus's resurrection but before He comes again. Satan has been condemned and judged but not yet imprisoned permanently.

The crucial question is this: **What does it mean to be a spiritually alive child of God living in an unredeemed, unrestored world?**

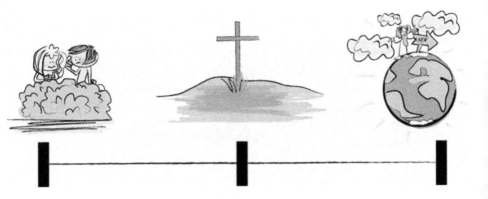

Getting To The Root

Some illnesses such as malaria or tonsillitis have a purely physical root. Others may have a spiritual root. Still others may have a mental or emotional root.

Conventional medicine and sometimes our approach to healing in the Church can sometimes be like pulling the heads off weeds but leaving the roots in place.

For example, a lady goes to the doctor with indigestion, gas, and nausea. Some investigations are arranged and stomach inflammation is diagnosed. Tablets are given to heal the stomach lining. A good doctor would also advise on lifestyle changes such as stopping smoking, reducing alcohol, and eating less spicy food.

Medicine in the West often stops here after addressing the physical issues. But we could dig deeper. Perhaps symptoms started after a stressful time when her husband left for someone else. She finds it hard to sleep and feels anxious and exhausted. The doctor might suggest counseling. She may get helpful advice about how to manage the anxiety, how to eat and exercise well, look after herself, and find new interests. All this is good.

We could dig deeper still and consider her spirit, the most fundamental part of her being. This rarely happens in the treatment plan because doctors have not been trained to consider the spiritual realm.

Might this lady be angry and bitter towards her husband? That would be perfectly understandable. But Jesus told a story in Matthew 18:21-35 to warn us that if we don't forgive from the heart, we will experience spiritual torment. If this is indeed the root, when the lady makes the choice to forgive her husband from her heart, it is likely that the anxiety and depression will start to improve, and the inflammation can heal.

Often physical symptoms can be a red flag waving to warn us that there may be something wrong at a deeper level.

Medical research backs this up. Two studies found "a significant association between the diagnosis of breast cancer and a behavior pattern, persisting throughout adult life, of abnormal release of emotions." In most cases, this was to do with suppressing emotions, especially anger[2]. A similar link was found with bowel cancer in those who repress anger and other negative emotions[3].

The Bible also links physical symptoms with deeper issues:

> A tranquil heart gives life to the flesh, but envy makes the bones rot. (Proverbs 14:30 ESV)

We're going to look in turn at our spirit, our mind, our emotions, our will, and our body. We'll then draw some conclusions about how we can become the people God wants us to be and do the things He has prepared for us to do. And we'll work out how we can approach seeking healing and wholeness in our own situations.

2 Greer, S. & Morris, T. (1975). Psychological attributes of women who develop breast cancer: A controlled study. *Journal of Psychosomatic Research*, 19, 147-153.
3 Personality as a risk factor in large bowel cancer: data from the Melbourne Colorectal Cancer Study GA Kune, S Kune, LF Watson. *Psychological Medicine* 1991, cambridge.org

PAUSE FOR THOUGHT 2

What experiences do you have of spiritual, mental, and emotional issues being the root cause of a physical health problem? How might we try to uncover the root cause of a particular problem?

Keys To Take Home

1. **We tend to look at the world based on our culture, education, and upbringing but we need to learn to look at it as God says it really is.**

2. **All sickness comes ultimately from Adam's choice to disobey God and to trust Satan's lies more than God's truth.**

3. **Jesus died and rose again for our wholeness, which means more than just physical health.**

4. **Being physically healthy is not a good enough end in itself.**

5. **God has a purpose for your life and specific things for you to do which He has prepared in advance.**

6. **Spirit, mind, and body issues can all affect health and we need to consider all three.**

7. **Rather than just addressing the surface issue, we need to be willing to identify and deal with the root problem.**

Why not meditate on a different one of these "Keys" each day in the coming week and ask God to help you understand how it applies to your own life and thinking?

GOING DEEPER

The "Going Deeper" section that you will find at the end of every session provides some questions for you to consider at home. They are designed to help you wrestle a little more with what has been taught during the session.

- In what ways have you focused purely on physical health rather than wholeness across your whole being, spirit, mind, and body?

- Consider what your reaction is when you are faced with illness in yourself or someone else. Where do you turn first? Do you, for example, seek spiritual help, physical help, alternative therapy help? Why do you make that choice?

- Have you considered before that physical symptoms may have a root at the spirit or mind level? Can you think of an example of that in your own experience?

- If you are currently facing a health issue, how deep are you willing to go in searching for and addressing possible roots of the condition? What might stop you from digging deeper?

Spiritually Alive

WHAT'S IT ABOUT?

OBJECTIVE:

To understand the benefits that come from having our spirits connected to God's Spirit.

To become aware of some dangers that might prevent us experiencing those benefits in our day-to-day lives.

To understand how to remove any influence the enemy might have gained in us through past sin.

FOCUS VERSE: "I have come that they may have life, and have it to the full." (John 10:10)

WELCOME

Do you tend to see yourself primarily as a "body with a spirit" or as a "spirit with a body"?

WORSHIP

Jesus died and rose again specifically so that we may have life to the full. Consider these verses and praise Him for His life:

> Jesus answered, "I am the way and the truth and *the life*. No one comes to the Father except through me. (John 14:6)

> For if, by the trespass of the one man, death reigned through that one man, how much more will those who receive God's abundant provision of grace and of the gift of righteousness *reign in life* through the one man, Jesus Christ! (Romans 5:17)

> Because through Christ Jesus the *law of the Spirit who gives life* has set you free from the law of sin and death. (Romans 8:2)

Video length: 35:05

Pause For Thought 1 comes in at 22:01.

Pause For Thought 2 comes in at 32:44.

WORD

A Question Of Life And Death

Before Adam and Eve sinned, their spirits were connected to God. They were totally accepted, completely secure; and had a great sense of significance. In short, they were whole and healthy.

When Adam disobeyed God, he died spiritually which meant that he lost the significance, security, and acceptance that came from being connected to God.

All of us were therefore born with our spirit disconnected from God.

So God sent Jesus who said:

"I have come that they may have life, and have it to the full." (John 10:10)

At the moment we turned to Jesus and made Him our Lord, our spirits were reconnected to God. They came back to life!

And that returned us to the position of Adam and Eve before they sinned, with our deepest needs for security, significance, and acceptance perfectly met in Christ.

The fact that your spirit – the "real you" – has been 100% restored to how God intended is potentially amazing news for your health, wholeness, and fruitfulness.

However, there are three significant dangers facing us that mean that we may not actually experience the full benefits of it.

Danger 1: We Can Live As Though Nothing Has Changed

Because we were born without the relationship to God as Father that we were always meant to have, we spent much of our lives as spiritual orphans.

We didn't feel secure. We were constantly searching for love and acceptance. We didn't know our true identity.

If you follow Jesus, you are an orphan no longer. You are now a son or daughter of the King of Kings, a prince or princess.

But it's easy to stay in that orphan mind-set. Perhaps you have been taught that your sins have been forgiven, but you still feel like the same no good, rotten person underneath – guilty, ashamed, condemned – with a sense that God is disappointed in you.

The New Testament no longer uses the word "sinner" to describe people who follow Jesus – even though we do still sin from time to time. The word it uses to describe us is best translated as "holy one".

"For our sake he made him to be sin who knew no sin, so that in him we might become the righteousness of God." (2 Corinthians 5:21 ESV).

You were not just *covered* with the righteousness of God as if, when God looks at you, He sees Jesus instead. No, you actually *became* the righteousness of God at the deepest level of your being. Which means that when God looks at you, He sees you as you actually are, and He delights in you!

But if you continue to believe the messages that the world out there throws at you, or if you tend to measure yourself by your past experiences or your present failures, you'll continue to live as an orphan.

No Longer Orphans

Father God, thank You that You did not leave me as an orphan. Thank You that I can now cry to You, "Abba, Father".

I refuse to believe the lie that I am an orphan.
I choose to believe the truth that I have been born into Your family and am now Your much-loved child.

I refuse to believe the lie that, in order for You to love me, I have to do things to please You.
I choose to believe the truth that You love me just as I am because You are love.

I refuse to believe the lie that I have to strive for Your attention.
I choose to believe the truth that You always give me Your full attention.

I refuse to believe the lie that You will reject me if I don't perform well.
I choose to believe the truth that You accept me completely even when I fail.

I refuse to believe the lie that I have to provide for myself.
I choose to believe the truth that You promise to give me everything I need.

I refuse to believe the lie that I can trust only myself.
I choose to believe the truth that You promise to help me and I can trust You completely.

I refuse to believe the lie that no one really knows me or cares about me.
I choose to believe the truth that You knew me before the creation of the world and that Jesus would have died just for me if I had been the only person who needed Him to.

I refuse to believe the lie that I have to compare myself to others.
I choose to believe the truth that I am unique and that You value and love me for who I am.

I refuse to speak badly of myself.
I choose to speak about myself the same way You speak about me.

I refuse to believe the lie that I deserve punishment or illness.
I choose to believe the truth that Jesus took all the punishment I deserved.

I declare that I want to be whole, well, and fruitful and, by Your grace, that is what I will be.

Amen.

Knowing Who We Are In Christ Is Vital

A study was carried out to work out how to help the Pima Indians of Arizona make positive lifestyle changes. One group was given health information about exercise and nutrition. Another group was given that too but also took part in regular discussions with local leaders on Pima culture and history which made them feel good about their heritage. A year later the group that took part in the discussions was doing better on weight, waist circumference, blood glucose levels and insulin levels. Improving their self-esteem had a significant effect on their behavior which in turn had a positive effect on their health[1].

How is your self-esteem? Or to put it another way, what beliefs do you have about yourself? Hopefully that you are a prince or princess, a child of God who is secure, significant, and accepted!

When we know our identity, we will live accordingly.

The world has a real focus on having great physical health. Might a better focus be knowing the truth and living accordingly?

---

1 (Venkat Narayan KM, Hoskin M, Kozak D, Kriska AM, Hanson AM, Pettitt DJ, et al. Randomized clinical trial of lifestyle interventions in Pima Indians: a pilot study. *Diabetic Medicine* 1998;15: 66-72.)

Danger 2: Not Realizing That We Reap What We Sow

> Do not be deceived: God cannot be mocked. A man reaps what he sows. (Galatians 6:7)

Our actions have consequences. God loves us and tells us what is good for us and what is bad for us. We will face the consequences of our choices. The covenant God made with Israel included blessings for obedience and curses for disobedience (Deuteronomy 28). These curses included disease and plague.

No matter how much we kid ourselves, for example, that eating and drinking sugary things is OK, sooner or later we will reap what we sow in terms of ill health. Being a Christian will not protect us from that.

- Egypt suffered deadly plagues when Pharaoh disobeyed God. (Exodus 7:14-11:10)
- King Uzziah's pride led him into disobedience and the consequence was leprosy. (2 Chronicles 26:16-20)
- Elymas the sorcerer was struck blind when he blatantly opposed God. (Acts 13:6-12)
- The Corinthians' sickness came from "eating and drinking judgment on themselves" because they were handling communion wrongly. (1 Corinthians 11:29-30)

Not all sickness comes from disobedience. But clearly some does.

Danger 3: We Can Allow The Enemy A Foothold In Our Life Through Sin And This Might Lead To Sickness

It's important to know that Satan does not have the power to march into your life at will and do you damage (1 John 5:18). You are a child of God and Satan cannot harm you – unless you let him.

When Jesus healed people, sometimes He simply healed the illness, the implication being that it had a purely *physical* root – a deformity or a virus perhaps.

However, in other healings He cast out a demon and then the person became well. The clear conclusion we can draw is that one possible cause of a health issue is that a demon has some kind of influence in a person's life.

In John 14:30 (ESV), Jesus says to His disciples, "I will no longer talk much with you, for the ruler of this world is coming. He has no claim on me..." What is the mechanism whereby Satan might get a claim on us?

"In your anger do not sin": Do not let the sun go down while you are still angry, and do not give the devil a foothold. (Ephesians 4:26-27)

Anger itself is not sinful – it's just an emotion – but if we don't deal with it in short order, it turns to bitterness which is a sin and we give the devil a "foothold" – a spiritual issue.

Paul explains in 1 Corinthians 6:15-17 that if a child of God, whose spirit is joined to God's Spirit, also joins with a prostitute, they become "one flesh". This is not just a *physical* bonding – they become *spiritually* bonded together. This spiritual bond can serve to draw us back to the same person or to the same sin again and again. It may also lead to sickness: the church in Thyatira is warned that sickness will come unless they repent of sexual immorality (Revelation 2:22-23).

The wonderful thing is that, no matter how many past sexual experiences you may have had or what they were, they do not change your new identity as a holy one, and you can take back any ground you have given to the enemy.

PAUSE FOR THOUGHT 1

"Yet to all who did receive him, to those who believed in his name, he gave the right to become children of God – children born not of natural descent, nor of human decision or a husband's will, but born of God." (John 1:12-13).

We often think of ourselves as having been "adopted" by God but the Bible more often talks about being "born" again as His children. What difference does it make to you to know that you have actually been *born* into God's family rather than simply *adopted* by Him?

Taking Back Ground From The Enemy

> Submit yourselves, then, to God. Resist the devil, and he will flee from you.
> (James 4:7)

When we confess sin and turn back to God, we submit. But we also need to *resist* and take back the ground we have given him. Only then does he flee from us.

The Steps to Freedom In Christ (a booklet by Dr. Neil T. Anderson) is a tool that you can use to do that. It's good to do it regularly – it's the spiritual equivalent of the annual service for your car!

You ask the Holy Spirit to show you across the whole of your life where the enemy has a "claim" on you through past sin. You then submit and resist. At which point you can expect any illness caused by a spiritual issue to be resolved.

Step One: Counterfeit Versus Real
This deals with false guidance, participation in occult practices, and false religions.

Step Two: Deception Versus Truth

Step Three: Bitterness Versus Forgiveness

Step Four: Rebellion Versus Submission

Step Five: Pride Versus Humility

Step Six: Bondage Versus Freedom
This deals with habitual sins including sexual sins.

Step Seven: Curses Versus Blessings
This is about issues from previous generations – it can be that our parents' or grandparents' sin gave Satan a right to influence not just them but also us.

When psychologists carried out three pilot studies on people who had gone through *The Steps To Freedom in Christ*, the results showed an astonishing 40-50% improvement after three months in key areas of mental health such as depression, anxiety, fear, anger, tormenting thoughts, negative habits, and self-esteem.

Taking action at the spiritual level resulted in a positive change at the level of mental health. The figures below show the average percentage improvement.

	Depression	Anxiety	Inner Conflict	Tormenting Thoughts	Addictive Behaviour
Study 1	64%	58%	63%	82%	52%
Study 2	47%	44%	51%	58%	43%
Study 3	52%	47%	48%	57%	39%

Studies administered by Judith E. King, LMSW, ACSW, Sonlife Associates, Grand Rapids, MI, USA

Psychiatric Conditions

In Luke 8:26-39 Jesus meets a man who nowadays would be classed as psychiatrically ill but the Bible is clear that his particular condition was caused by demons. Jesus didn't give him medication or lock him up – He set him free by delivering him from the evil spirits that were tormenting him, so he was "in his right mind".

Psychiatric patients are often tormented by voices in their mind. The voices tend to be violent (telling them to kill themselves or others), or condemning ("you are useless, dirty, shameful, guilty"), or bring fear. The worldview in secular psychiatry does not allow for the possibility that those voices might be coming from a demon. A Biblical worldview would acknowledge the possibility that the voice someone is hearing could be from the enemy.

It's a revelation for some people when they realize the negative voices in their head are not necessarily their own and they do not have to listen to them.

Western medicine has discovered that in schizophrenia and other psychiatric illnesses there can be an imbalance in the interaction of the serotonin, dopamine, and noradrenaline chemical pathways (though it isn't clear whether the chemical imbalance causes the symptoms or whether the symptoms cause the imbalance). Antipsychotic or antidepressant medication is used to try and bring balance, block the voices, or improve the mood, and can be very useful to help people with mental health problems stay stable and safe and function better. Much good work is done by mental health teams to manage severe mental health issues but we rarely see cure.

We are not saying that all psychiatric or mental illnesses are caused by spiritual issues. However, if we are going to adopt a Biblical worldview, it's a possibility that we need to consider.

And if that does turn out to be the case, then there is great hope for healing as people learn to take hold of their authority in Christ, submit to God, and resist the devil.

PAUSE FOR THOUGHT 2

In what ways can sin lead to health problems?

How could we prevent that happening?

Keys To Take Home

1. Don't focus primarily on good health. Focus on knowing the truth and living accordingly.

2. Your spirit, "the real you", is now alive and connected to God.

3. Your deepest needs for security, significance, and acceptance are now perfectly met in Christ.

4. You are no longer an orphan. You are a child of God!

5. We reap what we sow – and that applies to health as much as any other area.

6. Unresolved sin issues can be a root of physical, mental, and emotional illness but it is straightforward to remove them.

7. We cannot say whether the root of a particular illness is spiritual, mental, or physical but we can rule out a spiritual root by going through a regular spiritual check-up such as *The Steps To Freedom In Christ*.

 **GOING DEEPER**

- "Therefore, if anyone is in Christ, he is a new creation. The old has passed away; behold, the new has come" (2 Corinthians 5:17 ESV). Spend some time (at least five minutes) in silence and consider the implications for your life of this statement of fact from the Bible.

- Repeat the following statement slowly to yourself four or five times: "I am a much-loved daughter [or son] of the King of Kings." Consider how you tend to see yourself, think about yourself, and talk about yourself. Do the thoughts you have about yourself agree with what God says about you in His Word? If not, where do you think they might come from? If thoughts you have are not true, do you have to keep on thinking them?

- Read the "No Longer Orphans" list on pages 35-36 slowly. Ask the Holy Spirit to highlight one or two truths from it that He wants you to think more about. Spend time meditating on them. Speak them out loud each day, or perhaps every time you have a drink or eat a meal.

Sound Mind

WHAT'S IT ABOUT?

OBJECTIVE:

To understand:

- what the "flesh" is and how it works;
- that difficult circumstances in the present are not in themselves the problem – it's how we perceive them;
- that traumatic events from the past are not in themselves the problem – it's the lies they caused us to believe.

To learn how:

- to take every thought captive;
- to renew your mind to God's Word, which is what will bring about lasting transformation.

FOCUS VERSE: Do not conform to the pattern of this world, but be transformed by the renewing of your mind. Then you will be able to test and approve what God's will is – his good, pleasing, and perfect will. (Romans 12:2)

WELCOME

Doctors agree that a significant proportion of medical symptoms are a direct result of what we think. Does that mean that those symptoms are not real ("all in the mind"), or might there be more to it?

WORSHIP

Praise God for His truth and worship Him because He is THE Truth (John 14:6):

- His word is the truth; (John 17:17)
- The Bible is the inspired Word of God; (2 Timothy 3:16)
- We have received the Spirit of truth (John 16:13).

Video length: 35:33

Pause For Thought 1 comes in at 14:50.

Pause For Thought 2 comes in at 32:33.

WORD

Thinking About Thinking

Paul tells us in Romans 12:2 that renewing our mind is the key to ongoing transformation as disciples of Jesus.

The mind is not the same thing as the brain: when we die, our brain will return to dust with the rest of our body but we will still have our mind. The mind and the brain work together like different parts of a computer. Computer hardware is like the brain – on its own it can't do much. It needs software to make it useful. And our mind is that software. Even the best software won't work on hardware that is malfunctioning which is why Alzheimer's disease is so tragic. But in the Bible the overwhelming emphasis is not on the hardware, it's on the software, on the mind. It's about choosing truth, taking every thought captive.

For as he thinks in his heart, so is he. (Proverbs 23:7 NKJV)

Response To Difficult Or Traumatic Circumstances

When we experience a stressful event, there is a physical response in our body: our heart beats faster; our mouth goes dry; we breathe faster; we experience a butterfly feeling in our stomach. This is the "fight or flight" response when our sympathetic nervous system is activated and our body is fueled with cortisol and adrenaline ready to fight or run.

This mechanism can literally save our lives but if it runs on over-drive it can be harmful. An overstimulation of adrenaline and cortisol weakens the immune system and is linked to asthma, eczema, headaches, heart irregularities, irritable bowel syndrome, and certain cancers.

But it's not the stressful event in itself that is the problem. The event is picked up by your senses and then passed through your mind, through the software. Your mind then interprets the data in a personal way based on previous experiences: memories and traumas you have experienced. It then feeds back the results to the brain, which triggers a particular reaction.

You are not so much affected by your environment and circumstances but by how you *perceive* your environment and circumstances.

Two people can respond to the same stressful situation in completely different ways depending on how their mind has been "programmed". For one person, the loss of a job might be seen as an exciting opportunity for a new challenge: "Bring it on!" Someone else might be crushed by it. Another person may suffer a series of nasty personal attacks and come to believe that they are useless. Someone else may suffer the same thing but choose to believe that the attacker is just a horrible person.

It's not the traumatic event itself that is the problem – it's the lie it causes you to believe.

The trigger for the fight or flight reaction doesn't have to be an actual event happening right now. It can be triggered by just thinking about someone we are angry with or a traumatic memory from the past. For example, if you were abused as a child by a man with a loud voice, when you hear a man raising his voice on television you may start to feel panicky. But it's not the man on the television causing the stress – it is the triggered memory or experience passed through your mind which (understandably but wrongly) has picked up the faulty belief that all men with loud voices are a danger.

In the story of David and Goliath both David and the Israelite army were confronted by the same stressful situation – but they looked at it completely differently. The soldiers saw the giant in relationship to themselves while David saw him in relationship to God. David saw the situation as it really was.

It's critical that our software is based on what is actually true from God's Word rather than what our past experiences tell us. As a follower of Jesus your identity is based not on your past experiences but on what God says about you.

PAUSE FOR THOUGHT 1

In what ways could our mind and our thinking influence our health? Can you think of examples from your own experience?

Look at the list of *Who I Am In Christ* on pages 57-58. How could knowing that these things are true have a positive effect on our health?

The Flesh

In 1979 a fascinating experiment began in Wales. 35 years on, the conclusion was that it delayed the development of heart disease by up to twelve years, and of dementia by around six years. Yet there was no new wonder drug. Participants just had to agree to do five simple things: eat well; exercise regularly; drink less alcohol; keep their weight down; and never smoke. 2,500 men volunteered to take part, but 35 years later, only 25 were still taking part in the study. The vast majority missed out on some truly spectacular health benefits[1].

Ephesians 2 helps us understand why we naturally tend towards making bad choices.

> As for you, you were dead in your transgressions and sins, in which you used to live when you followed the ways of this world and of the ruler of the kingdom of the air, the spirit who is now at work in those who are disobedient. (Ephesians 2:1-2)

Because we were born without the spiritual connection to God we were created to have, we looked for ways to meet our legitimate needs for significance, security, and acceptance elsewhere. That's why we naturally "followed the ways of this world", the system we grew up in. It comes to us and says, "Do you want to be significant? Get a good job. Do you want to be secure? Get a lot of money in the bank. Do you want to be accepted? Do what others want you to. Fit in."

All temptation is an attempt to get us to meet our legitimate needs for significance, security, and acceptance independently of God.

All of us also lived among them at one time, gratifying the cravings of our flesh and following its desires and thoughts. Like the rest, we were by nature deserving of wrath. (Ephesians 2:3)

Instead of following the leading of God's Holy Spirit, we learned to make our own way in the world and ended up following the desires and thoughts of what Paul calls "our flesh".

---

1 http://www.telegraph.co.uk/health/healthnews/11199403/Secret-of-healthy-ageing-discovered-in-ground-breaking-35-year-study.html

Because we were born disconnected from God's Spirit, we developed ways of trying to cope with what life throws at us – but without God. We did what felt good to us at the time.

Our brains contain dopamine receptors, some of which give us pleasurable feelings when they are fired by things such as sugar, alcohol, winning a bet, exercise, or sex. The pleasurable feelings they release make us feel better and therefore want to do the thing again.

Scientists now understand that the "wiring" in our brains – made up of neural pathways – is not fixed but is constantly changing. The more we repeat a pleasurable action, the stronger the neural pathway associated with that action becomes and the more the desire grows to do it again.

The same principle works with negative ways of thinking too. As we grow up, negative experiences may cause us to develop patterns of thinking such as "I'm useless" or "I'm dirty".

All of us are walking around with beliefs and assumptions we have grown up with but which are not true. It may be a thought that is obvious such as, "I am so ugly and unattractive."

It could be at a more subconscious level such as, "I am only of worth if I keep achieving." If I believe that, my self-esteem will be low so I may strive to please people and say the right things so that they will like me. This will mean that I will often feel anxious and fearful. My heart will race whenever I am with people and I may have lots of bowel symptoms. The root of the problem isn't physical – it's a faulty belief.

It's like a Land Rover that drives across a muddy field the same way every day making deep ruts that become baked in the sun. Eventually you could take your hands off the steering wheel and it would just follow the ruts. These ingrained thought patterns become our "default" ways of behaving. These make up what the Bible calls "the flesh."

If you knew where to look, you could put your brain under a microscope and identify the neural pathway responsible for your desire for chocolate! It's fascinating that what the Bible calls "the flesh" actually literally is flesh.

Neuroscientists have discovered that, if we make a choice not to perform a particular habit or action over a period of time, the neural pathway gets weaker and weaker and we have correspondingly less desire to do the action or think according to the particular thought pattern. The Biblical principle is:

> But I say, walk by the Spirit, and you will not gratify the desires of the flesh. (Galatians 5:16 ESV).

As we follow the promptings of the Spirit rather than those of the flesh, the desires of the flesh will get weaker and weaker as those neural pathways fade away. In other words we can choose to steer the Land Rover out of the ruts.

The more we choose to trust God and believe the truth, the more we will experience life, peace, and wholeness and the better choices we will make.

Stronghold-Busting

> The weapons we fight with are not the weapons of the world. On the contrary, they have divine power to demolish strongholds. We demolish arguments and every pretension that sets itself up against the knowledge of God, and we take captive every thought to make it obedient to Christ. (2 Corinthians 10:4-5)

Ingrained habitual ways of thinking, those deep ruts in our minds, are called "strongholds" in the Bible. God's clear promise is that we can demolish them and be set free to think according to the truth. Once you have been though *The Steps To Freedom In Christ* to resolve spiritual issues, a mental stronghold is simply a habit that can be broken.

1. Identify The Faulty Belief You Want To Change

That is what the Bible calls taking captive every thought to make it obedient to Christ. It means noticing what we are thinking and saying, and considering whether it is in line with what God tells us is true in His Word.

2. Consider What Effect Believing That Lie Is Having In Your Life.

Realizing the negative effects should spur us on to tear the stronghold down.

3. Make A List Of Key Bible Verses That Counteract The Lie.

Your past experiences may have left you with a sense that you are helpless and that it would be hopeless to try to change. But God's Word makes some clear statements that contradict that: God will never leave you or forsake you (Isaiah 41:10-13, Hebrews 13:5-6); You can do all things through Jesus who gives you strength (Philippians 4:13).

4. Write A Declaration Based On The Verses.

Use the following pattern:

"I refuse to believe the lie that... [eg I am dirty]

I speak out the truth that... [eg I have been washed clean by the blood of Jesus, that I am pure and holy, that I can draw near to God in full assurance etc.]"

5. Read The Declaration Out Loud Every Day For 40 Days.

The Bible says that "The tongue has the power of life and death!" (Proverbs 18:21) and speaking out loud seems to help our minds take hold of the truth more effectively than simply reading silently.

Be warned! Stronghold-Busting is not as easy as it may sound because the lie behind the stronghold feels absolutely true to you.

As you go through your 40 days, it's like a concrete wall being demolished. It withstands 10, 20, 30 blows with no visible sign of being weakened. As you work through it day after day, it will feel as if nothing is changing. However, eventually a few small cracks appear and then the cracks get bigger and finally the wall completely collapses. Even though only the final few swings appear to have had an effect, without the previous swings, the wall would not have fallen.

Free App With Stronghold-Buster Builder
You can download a free app that includes a Stronghold-Buster-Builder. It reminds you every day at a time of your choosing to make your declaration and brings it up on your screen. It also counts off the 40 days for you. Details are on page 8 or at FreedomInChrist.org/health.

Isn't This Just Cognitive Behavioral Therapy?
Stronghold-Busting has a lot of similarities with cognitive behavioral therapy, a methodology used widely in the secular world which also involves exchanging one thought for another. There are two crucial differences. First, it is so much easier to do this if we have first dealt with spiritual issues, because the spiritual power holding us back is gone. Second, we have a much better truth to replace the faulty thinking – we have the very word of God Himself!

Have you become aware of lies that you are prone to believe? What is the most significant one? Use this time to create – or start to create – your very own Stronghold-Buster so that you can go on to demolish it. Use the guidelines on page 53 and take note of the sample Stronghold-Busters on pages 59–61. There is space to create your own Stronghold-Busters on pages 62–67. You can also use our app (see page 8).

Keys To Take Home

1. **What we believe and how we think have a significant effect on our physical body.**

2. **Our minds have been "programmed" with faulty information ("the flesh") and that does not automatically change when we become Christians.**

3. **Every day we can choose either to listen to the promptings of the Holy Spirit or to listen to the faulty programming of the flesh.**

4. **It's crucial that we learn to notice what we are thinking and we reject thoughts that do not line up with what God tells us is true, whether it *feels* true or not.**

5. **It is not your actual circumstances that are the problem, but how you perceive them.**

6. **It's not the traumatic event from the past itself that is the main ongoing issue – it's the lies it caused you to believe.**

7. **Ingrained faulty beliefs can be changed. It takes time and effort, but you really will be transformed if you renew your mind to the truth in God's Word.**

GOING DEEPER

- At the end of each day, take five minutes to review how your old worldview has reared its head during the day to try to persuade you to compromise the truth of the Bible. When you identify it happening, take time to renounce the false belief from your previous worldview and make a commitment to base your life on the truth of the Bible.

- "You are not so much affected by your environment and circumstances but by how you *perceive* your environment and circumstances." Spend some time telling God about the difficult circumstances in your life. Ask Him to show you how He sees them and take some time to listen for His response.

- "It's not the traumatic event itself that is the problem – it's the lie it causes you to believe." Think about one or two of the difficult events from your past. Ask God to show you some of the things they caused you to believe about yourself and about Him. Are those things actually true according to His Word? Do they lead you to behave in particular ways?

Who I Am In Christ

I Am Accepted

I refuse to believe the lie that I am rejected, unloved, or shameful. In Christ I am accepted.

God says:

I am God's child. (John 1:12)

I am Christ's friend. (John 15:14-15)

I have been justified. (Romans 5:1)

I am united with the Lord and I am one spirit with Him. (1 Corinthians 6:17)

I have been bought with a price: I belong to God. (1 Corinthians 6:19–20)

I am a member of Christ's body. (1 Corinthians 12:27)

I am a saint, a holy one. (Ephesians 1:1)

I have been adopted as God's child. (Ephesians 1:5)

I have direct access to God through the Holy Spirit. (Ephesians 2:18)

I have been redeemed and forgiven of all my sins. (Colossians 1:14)

I am complete in Christ. (Colossians 2:10)

I Am Secure

I refuse to believe the lie that I am guilty, unprotected, alone, or abandoned. In Christ I am secure.

God says:

I am free from condemnation. (Romans 8:1–2)

I am assured that all things work together for good. (Romans 8:28)

I am free from any condemning charges against me. (Romans 8:31–34)

I cannot be separated from the love of God. (Romans 8:35–39)

I have been established, anointed, and sealed by God. (2 Corinthians 1:21–22)

I am confident that the good work God has begun in me will be perfected. (Philippians 1:6)

I am a citizen of heaven. (Philippians 3:20)

I am hidden with Christ in God. (Colossians 3:3)

I have not been given a spirit of fear, but of power, love, and self-control. (2 Timothy 1:7)

I can find grace and mercy to help in time of need. (Hebrews 4:16)

I am born of God and the evil one cannot touch me. (1 John 5:18)

I Am Significant

I refuse to believe the lie that I am worthless, inadequate, helpless, or hopeless. In Christ I am significant.

God says:

I am the salt of the earth and the light of the world. (Matthew 5:13–14)

I am a branch of the true vine, Jesus, a channel of His life. (John 15:1,5)

I have been chosen and appointed by God to bear fruit. (John 15:16)

I am a personal, Spirit-empowered witness of Christ's. (Acts 1:8)

I am a temple of God. (1 Corinthians 3:16)

I am a minister of reconciliation for God. (2 Corinthians 5:17–21)

I am a fellow worker with God. (2 Corinthians 6:1)

I am seated with Christ in the heavenly realms. (Ephesians 2:6)

I am God's workmanship, created for good works. (Ephesians 2:10)

I may approach God with freedom and confidence. (Ephesians 3:12)

I can do all things through Christ who strengthens me! (Philippians 4:13)

I am not the great "I Am," but by the grace of God I am what I am. (See Exodus 3:14; John 8:24, 28, 58; 1 Corinthians 15:10.)

Stronghold-Buster Example 1
Taking Comfort In Food Rather Than God

The lie: that overeating brings lasting comfort.

Effects in my life: harmful to health; getting overweight; giving the enemy a foothold; stopping my growth to maturity.

Proverbs 25:28: Like a city whose walls are broken through is a person who lacks self-control.

Galatians 5:16: So I say, walk by the Spirit, and you will not gratify the desires of the flesh.

Galatians 5:22–24: But the fruit of the Spirit is love, joy, peace, forbearance, kindness, goodness, faithfulness, gentleness and self-control. Against such things there is no law. Those who belong to Christ Jesus have crucified the flesh with its passions and desires.

2 Corinthians 1:3–4: Praise be to the God and Father of our Lord Jesus Christ, the Father of compassion and the God of all comfort, who comforts us in all our troubles, so that we can comfort those in any trouble with the comfort we ourselves have received from God.

Psalm 63:4–5: I will praise you as long as I live, and in your name I will lift up my hands. I will be fully satisfied as with the richest of foods; with singing lips my mouth will praise you.

Psalm 119:76: May your unfailing love be my comfort.

God, I renounce the lie that overeating brings lasting comfort. I announce the truth that You are the God of all comfort and that Your unfailing love is my only legitimate and real comfort. I affirm that I now walk by the Spirit and do not have to gratify the desires of the flesh. Whenever I feel in need of comfort, instead of turning to foods I choose to praise You and be fully satisfied as with the richest of foods. Fill me afresh with Your Holy Spirit and live through me as I grow in self-control. Amen.

Mark off the days:

1	2	3	4	5	6	7	8	9
10	11	12	13	14	15	16	17	18
19	20	21	22	23	24	25	26	27
28	29	30	31	32	33	34	35	36
37	38	39	40					

Stronghold-Buster Example 2
Defining Myself By A Medical Condition

The lie: that the medical condition I have defines who I am (that I *am* arthritic, celiac, schizophrenic etc.).

Effects in my life: restricts what I see as possible; boxes me in medically; makes people look at me in a certain way; potentially feeds the medical condition.

Ephesians 1:1: Paul, an apostle of Christ Jesus by the will of God, To God's holy people in Ephesus, the faithful in Christ Jesus.

2 Corinthians 5:17: Therefore, if anyone is in Christ, the new creation has come: The old has gone, the new is here!

1 Corinthians 6:17: But whoever is united with the Lord is one with him in spirit.

1 Corinthians 2:16: For, "Who has known the mind of the Lord so as to instruct him?" But we have the mind of Christ.

1 John 3:1a: See what great love the Father has lavished on us, that we should be called children of God! And that is what we are!

Song of Songs 2:10 My beloved spoke and said to me, "Arise, my darling, my beautiful one, come with me."

Romans 8:37: No, in all these things we are more than conquerors through him who loved us.

I refuse to believe the lie that any illness, disease, or symptom in my body or mind defines who I am as a person.

I speak out the truth that my core identity is that of a holy one, a brand new creation in Christ. I am one with Him in spirit. I have the mind of Christ. I am a child of almighty God and all the resources of heaven are available to me. I am completely loved and my Father calls me His beloved who is beautiful.

Regardless of any symptom, illness or disease my body has, I am more than a conqueror through Jesus. From now on I choose to define myself in ways that agree with what God says about me and to trust Him to take care of me.

Mark off the days:

1	2	3	4	5	6	7	8	9
10	11	12	13	14	15	16	17	18
19	20	21	22	23	24	25	26	27
28	29	30	31	32	33	34	35	36
37	38	39	40					

Stronghold-Buster Example 3
Worrying Constantly About Physical Symptoms

The lie: that physical symptoms in my body are of greater importance or more powerful than God..

Effects in my life: focusing on health and illness all the time; keeps me trapped in fear; makes me anxious; stops me engaging with others and doing things God wants me to.

Romans 8:38-39: For I am convinced that neither death nor life, neither angels nor demons, neither the present nor the future, nor any powers, neither height nor depth, nor anything else in all creation, will be able to separate us from the love of God that is in Christ Jesus our Lord.

John 10:29: My Father, who has given them to me, is greater than all; no one can snatch them out of my Father's hand.

Psalm 139:5: You hem me in behind and before, and you lay your hand upon me.

Psalm 139:14: I praise you because I am fearfully and wonderfully made; your works are wonderful, I know that full well.

Psalm 139:16: Your eyes saw my unformed body; all the days ordained for me were written in your book before one of them came to be.

Philippians 4:6-8: Do not be anxious about anything, but in every situation, by prayer and petition, with thanksgiving, present your requests to God. And the peace of God, which transcends all understanding, will guard your hearts and your minds in Christ Jesus. Finally, brothers and sisters, whatever is true, whatever is noble, whatever is right, whatever is pure, whatever is lovely, whatever is admirable – if anything is excellent or praiseworthy – think about such things.

Hebrews 12: 1b-2a And let us run with perseverance the race marked out for us, fixing our eyes on Jesus, the pioneer and perfecter of faith.

Father God, I refuse to believe the lie that physical feelings or symptoms in my body are of greater importance than You or more powerful than You. I speak out the truth that You created all of me, including my body, and that I am fearfully and wonderfully made. Thank You that all the days You have ordained for me have already been written in Your book and that You promise to hem me in and protect me. I choose not to be anxious about physical symptoms, but to receive Your peace to guard my heart and mind. I choose to focus on things that are true, lovely, pure, excellent and praiseworthy and to fix my eyes firmly on You. Amen.

Mark off the days:

1	2	3	4	5	6	7	8	9
10	11	12	13	14	15	16	17	18
19	20	21	22	23	24	25	26	27
28	29	30	31	32	33	34	35	36
37	38	39	40					

My Stronghold-Buster 1

1. What lie do you want to tackle?

2. What effect does this faulty belief have on your life? How different would your life be if you replaced it with what is actually true?

3. List as many Bible verses as you can that state what God says is actually true and then pick the top seven or eight:

4. Write a prayer/declaration:

I refuse to believe the lie that:

I speak out the truth that:

5. Read the Bible verses and say the prayer/declaration out loud every day for forty days. You can set the Freedom In Christ app to remind you each day.

Mark off the days below:

1	2	3	4	5	6	7	8	9
10	11	12	13	14	15	16	17	18
19	20	21	22	23	24	25	26	27
28	29	30	31	32	33	34	35	36
37	38	39	40					

My Stronghold-Buster 2

1. What lie do you want to tackle?

2. What effect does this faulty belief have on your life? How different would your life be if you replaced it with what is actually true?

3. List as many Bible verses as you can that state what God says is actually true then pick the top seven or eight:

4. Write a prayer/declaration:

    I refuse to believe the lie that:

    I speak out the truth that:

5. Read the Bible verses and say the prayer/declaration out loud every day for forty days. You can set the Freedom In Christ app to remind you each day.

Mark off the days below:

1	2	3	4	5	6	7	8	9
10	11	12	13	14	15	16	17	18
19	20	21	22	23	24	25	26	27
28	29	30	31	32	33	34	35	36
37	38	39	40					

My Stronghold-Buster 3

1. What lie do you want to tackle?

2. What effect does this faulty belief have on your life? How different would your life be if you replaced it with what is actually true?

3. List as many Bible verses as you can that state what God says is actually true then pick the top seven or eight:

4. Write a prayer/declaration:

I refuse to believe the lie that:

I speak out the truth that:

5. Read the Bible verses and say the prayer/declaration out loud every day for forty days. You can set the Freedom In Christ app to remind you each day.

Mark off the days below:

1	2	3	4	5	6	7	8	9
10	11	12	13	14	15	16	17	18
19	20	21	22	23	24	25	26	27
28	29	30	31	32	33	34	35	36
37	38	39	40					

Healthy Emotions

 WHAT'S IT ABOUT?

OBJECTIVE:

To understand why God gave us emotions and how we can, over time, change negative emotions into positive ones.

To appreciate why God commands us to forgive others.

FOCUS VERSE: But the fruit of the Spirit is love, joy, peace, forbearance, kindness, goodness, faithfulness, gentleness and self-control. Against such things there is no law. (Galatians 5:22-23)

 WELCOME

Are you the sort of person who "wears their heart on their sleeve" (openly shows emotion) or do you tend towards the opposite? Why do you think that is?

WORSHIP

Focus on some of the attributes of our amazing God:

- Love (1 John 4:16)
- Kindness (Romans 2:4)
- Holiness (Isaiah 6:3)
- Light. (1 John 1:5)

Video length: 32:40

Pause For Thought 1 comes in at 13:17.

Pause For Thought 2 comes in at 30:08.

WORD

What Are Our Emotions?

Emotions are a gift from God. We cannot turn them on and off at will: we can't, for example, just decide to like someone we instinctively dislike. But God doesn't ask us to *like* people – He commands us to *love* them. And love is not an emotion – it's a choice. If we make that conscious choice to love someone, we may find that we'll eventually come to like them too.

Although you can't control emotions directly, you can change them over time, as you make a conscious choice to change what you can control. And you can control what you choose to believe.

Just as positive emotions such as peace can show us that we are walking in obedience to God's Word (Philippians 4:6-7), negative emotions function rather like the red warning light on the dashboard of your car. When that light comes on – when you feel anxious, angry, or depressed – it's a warning sign that there is something you need to look at, an adjustment that needs to be made. Ignoring the warning can lead to bigger problems over time. The appropriate response is to stop the car and find out what's wrong.

Jesus showed us how important it is to be honest about how we feel.
He wept at the grave of Lazarus and He wept when He looked at Jerusalem.

It's important to note that negative emotions can be caused by physical things like hormones or a viral illness. In our experience, however, most negative emotions don't have a physical root but are rooted in spirit or mind issues.

Why God Commands Us To Forgive

We have found that one of the main causes of negative emotions is unforgiveness.

Forgive as the Lord forgave you. (Colossians 3:13).

God commands us to forgive because He loves us and knows it is good for us:

Anyone you forgive, I also forgive. And what I have forgiven – if there was anything to forgive – I have forgiven in the sight of Christ for your sake, in order that Satan might not outwit us. For we are not unaware of his schemes. (2 Corinthians 2:10-11)

Unforgiveness gives the enemy a foothold in your life – a spiritual root that could conceivably be a doorway to illness. It also affects your thinking negatively, another root of physical problems.

The reason we find it so difficult to forgive is because we want to see justice done, don't we? Of course! We want them to pay for what they did.
We think that, in commanding us to forgive, God is asking us to sweep what was done under the carpet, to say it was OK. In fact it's the opposite:

Do not take revenge, my dear friends, but leave room for God's wrath, for it is written: 'It is mine to avenge; I will repay,' says the Lord." (Romans 12:19)

He promises that if you entrust the matter to Him, He will ensure that it is *not* swept under the carpet.

When you forgive, although you are letting the person off your hook, you are not letting them off God's hook. When you choose to forgive, you are taking a step of faith to trust God to be the righteous judge who will make everything right by demanding full payment for everything done against you.

Everyone who sinned against you will have to stand before God and explain it – either it will be paid for by the blood of Jesus if the person follows Jesus, or they will have to face the judgment of God if they're not.

So you can make the choice to hand all of that pain and those demands for justice over to God, safe in the knowledge that justice will be done. In the meantime you can walk free of it.

How Do We Forgive?

Jesus says we need to forgive from the heart (Matthew 18:35). That means being emotionally honest about what was done to us and just how much it hurt us. We have to face the pain and the hate that we feel. We have to be honest with God. In *The Steps To Freedom In Christ*, you do it like this: "Lord I choose to forgive [whoever it is] for [what they did or failed to do] which made me feel [this way or that way....]" And then you just tell God about every hurt and pain.

This isn't easy. But you do it in order to resolve this issue and get rid of the pain that you've been carrying around. We will continue to suffer spiritual torment, negative emotions, and possibly physical illness until we forgive.

We can't move on from the past until we forgive.

We won't be able to do what God has prepared for us to do until we forgive.

We won't be fruitful disciples until we forgive.

PAUSE FOR THOUGHT 1

We compared negative emotions to the red warning light flashing on the dashboard of your car. The appropriate response when the light comes on is to check to see what is wrong. If you feel angry, anxious, or depressed, how might you go about investigating what is wrong?

Depression

Most of us go through periods of feeling down or sad. And when we go through trauma, bereavement, or some other loss, it would be surprising not to feel sad.

A diagnosis of depression comes when you feel persistently sad for weeks or months, rather than just a few days. Don't think, however, that a diagnosis means staying depressed is inevitable. It isn't. Don't let a medical label define who you are or discourage you by making you think that you can't recover.

When you are depressed, you may find it difficult to concentrate and daily tasks feel difficult. Often you will lack energy and motivation and lose interest in things you would usually enjoy. You may sleep badly and find your appetite goes. Sometimes thoughts come into your mind of ending your life as a way out. These symptoms are very real, and you can't just "snap out of it".

Depression can have a purely physical root, for example, an underactive thyroid gland, certain hormone problems, or side effects of medications, so consulting a doctor is advised.

However, for most people no clear physical cause is identified, and it would then be appropriate to look for a root cause at the mind or spirit level.

If you are helping someone else, it helps to hear their story. Some good questions can be:

- When did you first feel like this?
- What happened at that time?
- What kind of things go round your mind repeatedly?
- Do you have nightmares?
- Do you get stuck in negative patterns of thinking?
- What is it usually about?
- Has anything traumatic happened, even a long time ago?
- What was home like?
- What did your family members model to you?

If you suffered some kind of sexual abuse as a child, you probably felt powerless, dirty, or ashamed and you may still feel like that because the negative thoughts have become part of your "programming". If you believe God wasn't there for you in the trauma, you probably question His love and your value now.

The root might be triggered by a loss in the present – of a job, relationship, or status. For example, if you have come to believe that your success as a person depends on how much you earn or achieve, and then you lose your job, you may feel you have lost your worth and value as a person and will probably feel depressed.

In both cases, the root is a faulty belief that can be changed. You're *not* dirty, powerless, or guilty. God *was* there and hated what happened to you. You can't change your past but you can choose to walk free from it. You are not defined by career success or how much money you have. You are defined by what Father God says about you.

Understanding that the real problem is a faulty belief gives hope for change. You can do something about it! You may not be able to change your circumstances or your past, but you can change how you see them. You can change those faulty beliefs for ones that are genuinely true.

Practical Steps

See a doctor

It is wise to seek medical advice. You may be prescribed anti-depressants. They can help us function better so that we can make the changes necessary to resolve the root issues. But medication can only treat the surface symptoms and there is a risk that we will be so pleased to feel better, that we don't take the next step and address the deeper issues.

Seek help from another person

A counselor, trusted friend or church leader perhaps. It's good to talk.

Address any possible spiritual roots by going through *The Steps To Freedom In Christ.*

Renew your mind using Stronghold-Busting.

Resolve that you do want to get well

Depression can become part of our identity. Being "ill" can also bring us support, love, care, and even money, that we may not be willing to give up.

Other Helpful Things

Friends who love you enough to be honest, real and challenging as well as supportive are a blessing! It is in the honesty and challenge, in a place where you feel safe and loved, that you can face your darkest secrets.

Worship really helps! In worship we direct our attention away from ourselves and towards God.

Make sure your life has balance and includes things like exercise, fun things, creative things, being outside in God's creation.

Laugh! The joy of the Lord really is our strength. Look for good things, choose to dwell on positive things, watch funny TV programs.

Be wise about who you spend time with. Some people drain us of energy and life. Others fill us up and we feel better when we are with them.

Be careful what you say. If you speak out negative things – "I am depressed" or "I am down" – then you will likely be what you say. This is not to pretend we are OK when really we are not. Rather it is to choose to speak what God says is true rather than what we feel. I could say: "I am a precious child of God who is very

loved, even though today I feel alone and unlovable." Or "I have not received a spirit of fear but one of power, love and a sound mind, even though today my mind is full of negative, fearful thoughts."

Look outside yourself to the needs of others. Volunteer to help the homeless, walk dogs from a rescue shelter, write to someone in prison.

Negative To Positive

As we relentlessly commit to believe what God tells us is true, we can expect the balance of emotions to shift from negative to positive. God's peace will assure us that we are walking with Him. The joy of the Lord really will be our strength.

PAUSE FOR THOUGHT 2

If you had a friend who was depressed, how might you begin to help them?

Keys To Take Home

1. **Negative emotions are a gift from God to alert us to faulty beliefs.**

2. **We can't control emotions directly, but we can change them over time as we choose to believe the truth.**

3. **Unforgiveness is a very common root cause of emotional and physical ill health.**

4. **God commands us to forgive so that we can stop hurting, prevent the enemy from holding us back, and receive healing.**

5. **When we choose to forgive from the heart, we are trusting God to ensure that justice is done while we walk free.**

6. **Depression that does not have a physical root can be resolved as we address the root causes, get appropriate medical input, deal with any spiritual issues, and renew our mind.**

7. **It's important not to get our identity from our illness, be honest about what we gain from it, and make a definite decision to want to be well.**

 **GOING DEEPER**

- Every day specifically commit yourself to walk by the Spirit and ask the Holy Spirit to fill you.

- Make a list of the negative emotions that you commonly experience. For each one, ask God to help you become aware of faulty beliefs that it might be highlighting. Do you think that changing those faulty beliefs might stop the negative emotions occurring?

- Read Psalm 13 and consider David's emotional honesty. Do you find it difficult to be emotionally honest and real? If so, ask the Holy Spirit to help you understand why that is.

- If you are facing a health issue, spend some time considering this crucial question: Do I really want to be well? Are there any benefits that come from being ill – perhaps attention, contact from others, finance? Is there any sense that the thought of becoming well feels at least a little scary? Tell God your conclusions.

Free To Choose

WHAT'S IT ABOUT?

OBJECTIVE:

To understand the importance God puts on free will, that the choices we make have real consequences, and that God delights in people who obey Him because they choose to, rather than out of any sense of compulsion.

To appreciate that, although we have been set free from slavery to sin, we can choose to return to slavery by letting sin "master" us.

To see how the Biblical principles of "Truth, Turning, and Transformation" taught on this course can enable any Christian to resolve addictive sin issues.

FOCUS VERSE:

Jesus replied, "Very truly I tell you, everyone who sins is a slave to sin. Now a slave has no permanent place in the family, but a son belongs to it forever. So if the Son sets you free, you will be free indeed." (John 8:34-36)

WELCOME

What do you think of when you hear the word "freedom"?

WORSHIP

Read Luke 4:18-19. Focus on the freedom that Jesus brings, the freedom that the Holy Spirit brings (2 Corinthians 3:17) and the freedom that God is bringing to the whole of Creation (Romans 8:21).

Video length: 33:12
Pause For Thought 1 comes in at 12:53.
Pause For Thought 2 comes in at 29:40.

WORD

Choices And Consequences

God gives us clear guidelines as to how we should live in the Bible. As C.H. Spurgeon said, "There is nothing in the law of God that will rob you of happiness: it only denies you that which would cause you sorrow."[1] The guidelines are there because God loves you and wants you to be fruitful and whole.

God could have set out His laws and then made us like robots so that if we wanted to disobey Him, perhaps criticize what someone else believes or lash out against them in anger, we'd find that we just couldn't do it – the words wouldn't come out or our fist would hit an invisible barrier an inch from their jaw. But He didn't do that.

Instead, He tells us the consequences of a particular choice, and then leaves us completely free to choose whether or not to obey.

---

1 Spurgeon, Charles H., *The Complete Works of C. H. Spurgeon, Volume 41: Sermons 2394-2445*, Delmarva Publications, Inc.

God delights in people who choose to obey Him, not because they feel they *have* to but simply because they love Him and they *freely choose* to.

God said to Adam and Eve, "You must not eat from the tree of the knowledge of good and evil, for when you eat from it you will certainly die" (Genesis 2:17). There's the guideline and the consequence. They were totally free to choose. But when they chose to disobey, their spirits did die. They reaped what they sowed.

Slaves To Sin

Adam and Eve's sin also had huge consequences for all their descendants, including us. We were all born spiritually dead, separated from God.

And that had a direct effect on our own ability to make good choices. Since we didn't have the Spirit of God to guide us and grew up following the ways of the world, we were inclined to disobedience. We developed all of that faulty programming that the Bible calls the flesh. We were looking for things that would help us get through life but without God.

We're told that the main reasons people become addicts are:
- trying to numb psychological or emotional pain, usually caused by past events;
- to try to cope with stress;
- they feel their life is somehow unsatisfactory;
- to overcome social inhibitions so that they can feel liked and fit in;

- they really dislike themselves and are in effect punishing themselves for something that's been done to them or something that they did.

To one extent or another, those applied to us all before we knew Jesus. We were "slaves of sin" (Romans 6:20). In other words, we were drawn to sin again and again as if it were a great big magnet.

There's a passage in Romans 7 where Paul describes exactly what it's like to be drawn to something that you know is wrong and ultimately harms you, but you just keep going back:

> I do not understand what I do. For what I want to do I do not do, but what I hate I do. (Romans 7:15)

The big question theologians ask about this passage is whether or not Paul is talking about himself before he knew Jesus or after. It puzzles them because, of course, if you follow Jesus, you have a new nature and a new identity. You are a whole new person. Your needs for acceptance, security, and significance are completely met in Jesus. He has taken away all your guilt and all your shame.

In 1 Corinthians 6:12 some of the Corinthians are quoting a saying, "I have the right to do anything." Paul doesn't contradict them but says this: "But not everything is beneficial. 'I have the right to do anything' – but I will not be mastered by anything."

In other words, even Christians who have been set free by Jesus can allow things to master them again, even things that are good and wholesome in themselves, if we cross a line and start using them to fill the place in our lives that is meant to be filled by God. When they start to exert a pull on us that we don't seem able to resist, we become slaves to sin again.

The start of the slippery slope is when we forget who we now are, when the enemy deceives us into sin which gives him a foothold, or when we don't take every thought captive and just follow our old default ways of thinking. Then we return to being a slave to sin.

So yes, a Christian who has been set free can be deceived into giving up their freedom. Paul certainly could be talking about his experience as a Christian.

God doesn't love us any less if we get into that situation, however. Our amazing new identity has not changed. There is still no condemnation from God. What's at stake is not our *salvation* but our *fruitfulness*.

Jesus came specifically to break the cycle, to overcome the power of that magnet:

> "Very truly I tell you, everyone who sins is a slave to sin. Now a slave has no permanent place in the family, but a son belongs to it forever. So if the Son sets you free, you will be free indeed." (John 8:34-36)

Are You In Danger Of Addiction?

Be aware of the possibility of developing a full-blown addiction. There are environmental, genetic, and spiritual factors that make some people more vulnerable to becoming full-blown addicts, but it's not inevitable for anyone and in Christ you can resolve addiction completely.

The most difficult step is to acknowledge that there is a problem. Here are seven danger signs to look out for:

1. You develop a tolerance to that substance or activity, so you need more of it to get the same effect.
2. You experience withdrawal symptoms when you don't use the substance or activity.
3. You find the substance or activity consumes increasing amounts of your time, money, or thought.
4. You have a persistent desire for the substance or activity.
5. You make unsuccessful efforts to cut down your use.
6. You realize it is affecting relationships or your work.
7. You find you continue to use the substance or do the activity despite knowing it's harming you.

If you recognize **three or more** of these, it suggests that your habit has started to control your life and you would be well-advised to seek help. Perhaps start by talking to a leader in your church. You can also access our extra film, *Freedom From Addiction*, at www.FreedomInChrist.org/health.

But if you recognize that you have a strong physical addiction to alcohol or other drugs, seek medical help. A medical detox won't resolve the pain or other issues that led to the addiction in the first place but it will give you space to enable you to do that.

We Have The Answer!

The harm caused by addiction is horrendous:

- In the USA alone, every 50 seconds somebody dies because of issues related to drug, alcohol, and tobacco abuse.
- For every death from alcohol there are 500 other people who are already suffering adverse health issues because of it – conditions such as cancers, high blood pressure, and liver cirrhosis – to say nothing of mental health problems and social issues like domestic violence, homelessness, and crime.
- In Europe and the United States, the death toll from obesity is second only to that from tobacco.
- One in four internet searches results in viewing pornography. God's gift of sexual intimacy is perverted into a compulsion that can affect our mental health and poison our marriage relationships.
- Children as young as 11 are addicted to casino games online. Debt, mental health issues, and family breakdown are common among long-term gamblers.

The Church has a mandate from Jesus to see the captives released. We hold in our hands the answer to addiction issues. Can you imagine what a huge positive effect there would be on healthcare around the world if we were able to help more people understand that in Christ they can recover their ability to make good choices?

I Will Not Be Mastered By Anything

Let's take care not to let *anything* master us, even things that aren't in themselves bad. Do you need a coffee to get going in the morning or several more to get through a busy day? What about those cookies? Or is the thought to check your phone constantly popping up in your mind when you are doing other things?

Let's be clear. It's OK to drink coffee and eat and have a phone! But we are all vulnerable to crossing a line and letting those things become unhealthy or even master us. We're all vulnerable to being drawn again and again to certain sins and losing the freedom that Jesus died to give us.

> Let us throw off everything that hinders and the sin that so easily entangles. And let us run with perseverance the race marked out for us, fixing our eyes on Jesus, the pioneer and perfecter of faith. (Hebrews 12:1b-2a)

Those who are mature, effective disciples have learned to deal ruthlessly with sin.

PAUSE FOR THOUGHT 1

"We are free to choose but our choices have consequences." Do you find that idea liberating or a little scary? Why?
How does it feel to be caught in a behavior that you don't seem to be able to stop doing?

Testimony From Steve:

"Part of the fruit of the Spirit is self-control. A little while ago I became frustrated that it wasn't as evident in my life as I would like it to be and I set about trying to work out what was wrong in my belief system so that I could renew my mind.
I knew I had a vulnerability for comfort eating – in fact the first ever Stronghold-Buster was something I wrote to help me with that (you can see it on page 59) and I have revisited it several times over the years.

But there were other areas too and I realized that I had become a little like the people Paul was addressing who were saying, "I have the right to do anything."

As a young Christian I was taught that I had to obey certain rules. In more recent years I have finally come to understand something of the message of God's grace: I don't have to obey rules to please Him – I am already pleasing to Him because of Jesus. If I do wrong, it doesn't change who I am or my relationship with Him. There really is no condemnation for me; or shame. God isn't blessed when I do things for Him just because I feel I *have* to. It's been incredibly liberating to know these amazing truths.

However, I realized that the pendulum had swung too far the other way and I wasn't paying enough attention to how I was living. The real question is not so much, "Can you do such and such a thing?" The more significant question is, "Can you stop?" I had allowed myself to become a slave to sin. That didn't change God's love for me or my new identity but it did mean that the enemy could hold me back.

After a lot of thought I worked out that the lie I wanted to correct through a Stronghold-Buster was, 'It doesn't matter how I live', and you can see it on the following pages."

Stronghold-Buster
Refusing To Return To Being A Slave To Sin

The lie: that it doesn't matter how I live.

Effects in my life: time wasted on things that are not important, lack of self-discipline, putting on weight; lack of joy in the Lord.

Proverbs 25:28: Like a city whose walls are broken through is a person who lacks self-control.

Colossians 2:20-23: Since you died with Christ to the elemental spiritual forces of this world, why, as though you still belonged to the world, do you submit to its rules: "Do not handle! Do not taste! Do not touch!"? These rules, which have to do with things that are all destined to perish with use, are based on merely human commands and teachings. Such regulations indeed have an appearance of wisdom, with their self-imposed worship, their false humility and their harsh treatment of the body, but they lack any value in restraining sensual indulgence.

2 Timothy 1:6-7: For this reason I remind you to fan into flame the gift of God, which is in you through the laying on of my hands. For the Spirit God gave us does not make us timid, but gives us power, love and self-discipline.

Galatians 5:16: So I say, walk by the Spirit, and you will not gratify the desires of the flesh.

Galatians 5:22-24: But the fruit of the Spirit is love, joy, peace, forbearance, kindness, goodness, faithfulness, gentleness and self-control. Against such things there is no law. Those who belong to Christ Jesus have crucified the flesh with its passions and desires.

Romans 8:12-13: Therefore, brothers and sisters, we have an obligation–but it is not to the flesh, to live according to it. For if you live according to the flesh, you will die; but if by the Spirit you put to death the misdeeds of the body, you will live.

1 Corinthians 6:12: "I have the right to do anything," you say – but not everything is beneficial. "I have the right to do anything" – but I will not be mastered by anything.

1 Corinthians 6:19-20: Do you not know that your bodies are temples of the Holy Spirit, who is in you, whom you have received from God? You are not your own; you were bought at a price. Therefore honor God with your bodies.

Romans 6:16-18: Don't you know that when you offer yourselves to someone as obedient slaves, you are slaves of the one you obey – whether you are slaves to sin, which leads to death, or to obedience, which leads to righteousness? But thanks be to God that, though you used to be slaves to sin, you have come to obey from your heart the pattern of teaching that has now claimed your allegiance. You have been set free from sin and have become slaves to righteousness.

I refuse to believe the lie that it doesn't matter how I live.

I speak out the truth that:
- **I am not my own, because I was bought by Jesus at great price;**
- **I belong to Christ Jesus and, having been set free from sin, am now a slave to righteousness;**
- **I have crucified the flesh with its passions and desires;**
- **I have died with Christ to the elemental spiritual forces of the world;**
- **God has given me a spirit, not of fear, but of power and love and self-discipline;**
- **My body is a temple of the Holy Spirit.**

Therefore:
I present myself now to obedience to God and I present the parts of my body to God as an instrument of righteousness. By the Spirit I put to death the deeds of the flesh. Even though "I have the right to do anything," I refuse to let anything other than Jesus be my master. I declare that Jesus Christ is my Lord. I fan into flame the gift of God which is in me and choose to live by the Spirit, so that I will not gratify the desires of the flesh. I choose:
- **to be disciplined in what I eat and drink;**
- **to exercise my body so that I may better serve my Lord;**
- **to be discriminating in what I watch on TV.**

Lord God, please fill me afresh with your wonderful Holy Spirit and lead me in Your ways throughout this day. Be glorified in Your servant. Have Your way in me. Amen.

1	2	3	4	5	6	7	8	9
10	11	12	13	14	15	16	17	18
19	20	21	22	23	24	25	26	27
28	29	30	31	32	33	34	35	36
37	38	39	40					

Truth, Turning, Transformation

Don't you know that when you offer yourselves to someone as obedient slaves, you are slaves of the one you obey – whether you are slaves to sin, which leads to death, or to obedience, which leads to righteousness? But thanks be to God that, though you used to be slaves to sin, you have come to obey from your heart the pattern of teaching that has now claimed your allegiance. You have been set free from sin and have become slaves to righteousness. (Romans 6:16-18)

Paul is saying that you are either a slave to sin or a slave to righteousness. And it starts when you offer yourself to sin or righteousness. It's saying in effect "Here you are sin or righteousness, I give myself to you." In any area of your life you are either free or bound. You don't grow into freedom. You take possession of it.

The great statement of fact in the passage is, "you have been set free from sin." That is in the past tense. At any given moment we no longer have to sin.

I am now dead to sin and alive to God. I may still have the vulnerability and I will still be tempted. But at any given moment I can choose whether to follow the flesh or the Spirit of God.

"Blessed are those who hunger and thirst for righteousness, for they will be filled." (Matthew 5:6).

There is no greater satisfaction than living a righteous life. In this course we are equipping you with tools not just to help you be physically healthy but to enable you to be fruitful. We like to describe the approach with three "T"s: Truth, Turning Transformation:

TRUTH

The key to freedom is knowing the truth in God's Word in your heart not just your head. Most fundamental is knowing your new identity in Jesus. It's especially important to know that, when we fall into sin, nothing changes. God does not come to us in anger and say, "You're a sinner!" He probably says something like, "Hey you're *not* a sinner, you're my child, you're a holy one. So why are you *acting* like a sinner?"

If you are a follower of Jesus, your fundamental identity is not that of a sinner, a failure, an alcoholic, or an addict. Your fundamental identity is as a holy one, a beloved child of God Himself even when your behavior is not what you would want it to be.

When you know who you really are, you will live accordingly. Why not take the list of *Who I Am In Christ* (pages 57-58) and declare it out loud every morning for 6 weeks or until you know in your heart that every one of those statements really does apply to *you*?

TURNING
When you sin, you give the enemy influence in your life and he will hold you back. But it's straightforward to close the door you opened to him, know that all is still well between you and God, and just carry on.

Doing *The Steps To Freedom In Christ* on a regular basis will help you keep short accounts with God and kick the enemy out of your life. You don't have to do the whole thing. Just use the relevant part when you fall.

TRANSFORMATION
It's crucial to uncover the lies we are believing that led us into the sin so that we can renew our minds, using Stronghold-Busters. Remember that these take time and effort but are absolutely worth it.

The Habit Loop

These addictive behaviors tend to follow a repeating pattern often called "habit loops[2]". They start with a trigger, a circumstance that starts the tempting thought process or makes us feel particularly vulnerable. Part of taking every thought captive is learning to recognize these habit loops and disrupt them by not following the trigger thought.

If we unthinkingly act on the trigger, it leads to an action. And that leads on inevitably to indulging our addiction and getting its short-lived reward. And the whole habit loop waits to begin again: Trigger – Action – Reward.

When you understand the triggers, you can plan a different action when they fire. You could adjust your shopping habits or avoid friends you find difficult. You could go home another way to avoid the casino or find a more healthy way to get that reward: phone a friend; put on music; do some exercise.

Having someone you can be accountable to can really help. Just getting a phone call once a week asking how you are doing can be a great encouragement towards self-control.

There are excellent recovery groups that you can access, many with a Christian base. There are accountability websites where you can get blocks on sites that are tempting for gamblers or those with porn issues.

2 The phrase was popularized by Charles Duhigg in *The Power of Habit*, Random House, 2012, and is based on research done at Massachusetts Institute of Technology.

Things To Remember Not To Forget!

In conclusion, remember just who you now are: a slave to righteousness! Remember that living a righteous life in the power of the Spirit of God is the only way to true peace and satisfaction. Remember that failure is an *incident*, not an *identity*. God is cheering you on – loving you no matter how many times you slip.

And let's look wider than our own lives. The Church has a mandate from Jesus to see the captives released. We hold in our hands the answer to addiction issues. Imagine what a huge positive effect there would be on healthcare around the world if we were able to help more people know that in Jesus Christ they can recover their free will, which is the ability to make good choices.

PAUSE FOR THOUGHT 2

How does it feel to be caught in a behavior that you don't seem to be able to stop doing?

If a Christian were caught in a behavior they did not seem to be able to escape from, what course of action would you suggest to them?

Extra Film: *Freedom From Addiction*

There is an additional 24 minute film available for those who want to look at the topic of addiction in a little more depth.

View it at:
www.FreedomInChrist.org/health

Keys To Take Home

1. **God's rules and guidelines are for our good.**

2. **We are free to choose but our choices have consequences.**

3. **God is blessed by people who obey Him because they *want* to rather than because they feel they *have* to.**

4. **We can get addicted to things that make false promises to meet our legitimate needs for security, significance, and acceptance.**

5. **We used to be "slaves to sin" but Jesus has set us free so that at any given moment we can choose not to sin.**

6. **Applying the model of Truth, Turning, and Transformation will help us resolve negative behaviors that seem to control our lives.**

7. **Becoming aware of our particular vulnerabilities and triggers and taking appropriate steps to reduce their effect is crucial.**

 GOING DEEPER

- Take some time with God and ask Him to show you the areas in your life where you are vulnerable to being a "slave to sin". What behaviors or substances do you tend to turn to for comfort, to numb pain, to overcome inhibitions, or to cope with stress? Can you identify which deep needs you are trying to meet?

- Work out the habit loop for each one. What circumstances tend to trigger it? What will you do differently next time those circumstances arise?

- Be honest with yourself. Is there a sin that you feel you can't escape from? Have you tried to give it up and failed? Can you say no? Can you stop? Remember, this changes nothing about who you are in Christ or God's love for you. What steps will you take to begin to resolve this? Who could come alongside you to encourage you to make good choices?

FREEDOM IN CHRIST

Living Sacrifice

WHAT'S IT ABOUT?

OBJECTIVE:

To understand how to live as effective disciples in physical bodies that are gradually decaying.

To appreciate that, even though our physical bodies are just temporary accommodation for our time on earth, we need to take good care of them because God created them; they are the temple of the Holy Spirit, and they enable us to do the things God has prepared for us to do.

FOCUS VERSE: Therefore, I urge you, brothers and sisters, in view of God's mercy, to offer your bodies as a living sacrifice, holy and pleasing to God – this is your true and proper worship. (Romans 12:1)

WELCOME

Here are some facts about the human body:

* Between birth and death, the number of bones reduces from 300 to just 206.
* There are more bacteria in your mouth than there are people in the world.
* Laid end to end, an adult's blood vessels would go around the equator four times.
* A human heart beats over three billion times in an average lifetime.
* Humans shed around 600,000 particles of skin every hour and your outer layer of skin completely replaces itself approximately once a month.
* Your nose can differentiate between around one trillion different smells.

What is the most amazing and fascinating aspect of the human body to you?

WORSHIP

Worship God as the Creator and Master Designer. See Psalm 148:2-5, Nehemiah 9:6, Revelation 4:11.

Video length: 34:20

Pause For Thought 1 comes in at 15:47.

Pause For Thought 2 comes in at 31:45.

WORD

Wonderfully Made

> For you formed my inward parts; you knitted me together in my mother's womb. I praise you, for I am fearfully and wonderfully made. (Psalm 139:13-14a ESV)

Our bodies are amazing! There are so many different parts working in harmony, all sorts of chemicals, hormones, and enzymes fulfilling incredibly complex roles. They keep your heart beating, lungs breathing, bowels digesting, and kidneys removing waste. All without you even thinking about it.

Inside every cell in your body is an elaborate coding system of DNA two meters (2.2 yards) long. It determines things as diverse as your eye color and your aptitude for mathematics. In the nucleus of a cell our genes are arranged along twisted, double-stranded molecules of DNA called chromosomes. It's a superb, incredible piece of engineering, of creation.

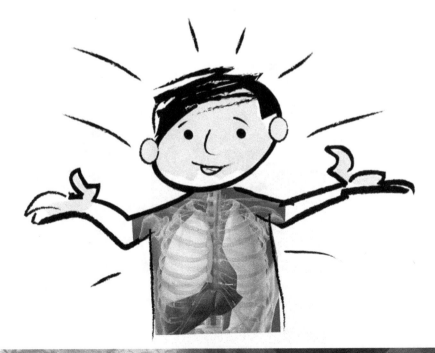

Effects Of The Fall

Originally our bodies seem to have been designed to go on forever renewing themselves. But Adam's sin had absolutely catastrophic effects on them. His body began to age and decay, so that physical death became inevitable. Even so, he lived for 930 years.

A good place to see something of the actual mechanism involved in the decay of our bodies as we get older is at the ends of your chromosomes where you will find complex structures called "telomeres". They protect the strands of DNA, rather like the plastic tips on the end of shoe laces. Each time a cell divides, the telomeres get shorter until eventually they get too short to do their job. And that appears to be a factor in why we get old and die – or at least a symptom of other processes going on at the level of our genes. It would be reasonable to assume that, before the Fall, the telomeres did not shorten.

There were other physical effects of the Fall. For example, women's pain in childbirth was significantly increased (Genesis 3:16).

We also became vulnerable to viruses and harmful bacteria. The Bible is clear that everything that was created, was created through Jesus and was "very good". So those viruses and bacteria presumably existed – at least in some form – before

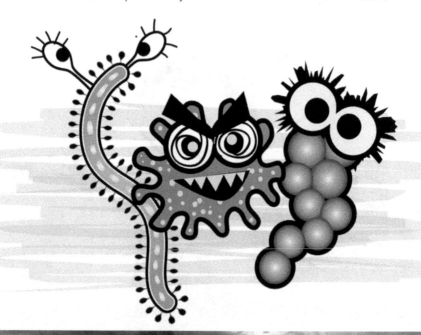

Adam sinned. They must originally have been harmless to us or perhaps had a good purpose, like the helpful bacteria in our gut that help us digest food. Or perhaps our immune system was originally so good that any virus would simply not pose a threat.

The Future Era

The Bible tells us that a time will come again when things that are currently harmful to us won't harm us any more:

> The wolf shall dwell with the lamb, and the leopard shall lie down with the young goat, and the calf and the lion and the fattened calf together; and a little child shall lead them... The nursing child shall play over the hole of the cobra, and the weaned child shall put his hand on the adder's den. (Isaiah 11:6, 8 ESV)

The Fall affected the whole of the created order. We're told that the whole of creation "groans" (Romans 8:22) – things like earthquakes and destructive weather systems are no doubt part of that.

The great news is that in the future era after Jesus returns there will be a new heaven and a new earth (Isaiah 65:17, Revelation 21:1).

We are also going to get brand new bodies (1 John 3:2, 1 Corinthians 15:51-52).

What About Right Now?

What does it mean to be a redeemed, restored child of God, living in an unredeemed, unrestored world as far as our physical bodies are concerned?

We still have the same old bodies. Paul wrote to the Corinthian church about how tough life can be as a Christian: "afflicted in every way, persecuted, struck down" (2 Corinthians 4:8 ESV). He is referring primarily to the difficulties that come when we are preaching the good news in the face of strong opposition. Yet what also comes through is the sheer weakness of just living in our human bodies. He talks of having "treasure in jars of clay" and says "We always carry around in our body the death of Jesus, so that the life of Jesus may also be revealed in our body." (2 Corinthians 4:10)

So let's face reality. Living in these mortal bodies can be really tough! They are slowly decaying. Ultimately our physical bodies are going to die. However, for us that's absolutely not the end of the story! The passage continues:

> Therefore we do not lose heart. Though outwardly we are wasting away, yet inwardly we are being renewed day by day. For our light and momentary troubles are achieving for us an eternal glory that far outweighs them all. So we fix our eyes not on what is seen, but on what is unseen, since what is seen is temporary, but what is unseen is eternal. (2 Corinthians 4:16-18)

If you think this life and this body is all there is, then it's incredibly depressing when physical frailty and mortality make their presence felt. But, as always, we must train ourselves to look at the world the way God says it actually is.

The physical frailty of our bodies actually allows God's glory to be shown in us. When we face physical infirmity, it isn't necessarily something we should be looking to "pray out of the way". It might be something through which God will reveal His greatness as we persevere through it in our weakness.

> For we know that if the earthly tent we live in is destroyed, we have a building from God, an eternal house in heaven, not built by human hands. .... while we are in this tent, we groan and are burdened....... (2 Corinthians 5:1-4)

He has a great analogy for our bodies: "the earthly tent we live in." In other words they are *temporary* accommodation for us. This is in contrast to something much more permanent that is coming which he calls: "an eternal house in heaven, not built by human hands." The difference between a flimsy tent and a solid building with foundations is huge.

The world is obsessed with "the body beautiful", thinking that we *are* our body and that the be-all and end-all is to have a healthy body. But it's just a flimsy, temporary thing. Something much better is coming. We are not "a body with a spirit" but "a spirit with a body."

While we are in this body, we "groan and are burdened." We may not realize it, but we are inwardly yearning for how it is meant to be: a body that does not decay, does not suffer sickness, that lasts for ever.

He continues by saying that God "has given us the Spirit as a deposit, guaranteeing what is to come" (2 Corinthians 5:5). As you see the fruit of the Spirit growing in your life, it's irrefutable proof that a brand new body will one day be yours.

Rather than adopting the worldly goal of having perfectly healthy bodies that go on and on, our aim is to use our physical bodies to glorify God as long as we remain in them. And that doesn't depend on being in perfect health.

Our bodies enable us to function on this earth as disciples of Jesus and do the things He has prepared for us to do. We can use them for good or for ill, for eternal purposes or for frivolous purposes. You have one life and one body. How are you going to use them?

PAUSE FOR THOUGHT 1

What practical difference might it make to see yourself as a "spirit with a body" rather than as a "body with a spirit"?

"When we face physical infirmity, it isn't necessarily something we should be looking to 'pray out of the way'." What is your opinion of this statement?

A Temple Of The Holy Spirit

Our body may be just a temporary home but that doesn't mean it's unimportant.

> Or do you not know that your body is a temple of the Holy Spirit within you, whom you have from God? You are not your own, for you were bought with a price. So glorify God in your body. (1 Corinthians 6:19-20 ESV)

Your body is a temple of the Holy Spirit, a holy place, and you are a holy one. We glorify God in our bodies when we live according to who we are, so it's important to take diet, exercise, and rest seriously.

Diet

God created all food for us to enjoy but we are warned against overeating.

Giving up sugar and processed foods and moving to a diet strong in vegetables and fruits is a good way to a healthier you. If we find we struggle to eat more healthily, we may need to uncover the root cause. If deep down we feel unhappy or dislike ourselves, we may be trying to fill the void with food.

Jesus spent a 40-day period in the wilderness being tempted during which He didn't eat a thing (Luke 4:2). Fasting is a spiritual discipline and is usually undertaken as a result of a leading from God. When we fast, we choose to abstain from food and certain pleasures for a given time, in order to seek closer intimacy with God in prayer and study of God's Word. As a bonus, this also gives our physical body a chance to clear itself of toxic waste. Several studies suggest that regular fasting may improve blood sugar, and help lower blood pressure and cholesterol levels, thereby enhancing heart health. Other health benefits associated with fasting include decreased levels of inflammation in the body, better brain function, and better metabolism, which may lead to improved success with weight loss. But don't fast for the health benefits alone. Fast primarily to deepen your intimacy with God and your dependence on Him. He loves us whether we fast or not.

Exercise

Paul says that "physical training is of some value" (1 Timothy 4:8) and regular exercise decreases the risk of developing health problems such as diabetes, heart disease, cancer, and depression as well as helping sleep and generally making you feel better.

A study by Leipzig University[1] found that, after six months of regular aerobic exercise, people's telomeres lengthened by 3.5%.

1 Reported in *The Telegraph*, 28 November 2018

There isn't a great deal in the Bible about exercise, however, simply because ordinary life was physical and active: walking was the main form of transport and most jobs involved physical labor. Most of us today have to make a definite choice to build physical activity into our lives. A key is finding something you enjoy. Dare to try something new!

Rest

> It is no use for you to get up early and stay up late, working for a living. The Lord gives sleep to those he loves. (Psalm 127:2 NCV)

Too little sleep can contribute to heart problems, strokes, weight gain, diabetes, and thyroid problems. In our busy society, however, it can be seen as a good thing to "burn the candle at both ends." Even in our churches, it can seem that the busier we are, the more we are valued and accepted.

God, however, considers rest so important that He made it one of the Ten Commandments (Exodus 20:8-11). Rest is not just about sleep. It is about allowing our inner beings to stop and rest too.

> He makes me lie down in green pastures, he leads me beside quiet waters, he refreshes my soul. (Psalm 23:2-3a)

We need to give space and time for our inner beings to be restored. Otherwise we are likely to burn out. Satan will constantly try and deceive us into believing it is unnecessary and that **doing** is much better than **being**.

Technology can rob us of rest and distract us, making space and silence seem scary.

Developing good habits takes effort and determination, but the benefit we gain is worth it. We need our physical bodies to be as healthy as possible so that we can do the things He has called us to do.

Even if you have a great diet and a fantastic exercise regime, and are in the best possible shape, it's impossible to predict with any certainty who will live to a grand old age and who will die an untimely death due to other causes. In the light of that, let's take note of Paul's exhortation to us:

Therefore, I urge you, brothers and sisters, in view of God's mercy, to offer your bodies as a living sacrifice, holy and pleasing to God – this is your true and proper worship. (Romans 12:1)

PAUSE FOR THOUGHT 2

Are there changes that you feel prompted to make in the areas of diet, exercise, and rest? If you feel comfortable to do so, share them with the group.

It can be difficult to make and maintain lifestyle changes. What are some practical ways that we could encourage and help each other?

Keys To Take Home

1. Our bodies are created according to an amazing design.

2. I am not my body: it is my temporary accommodation on earth.

3. Having a weak and frail body is no barrier to God demonstrating His great strength and glory in us.

4. Our bodies are the temple of the Holy Spirit and we are to glorify God in them.

5. Our goal is not to idolize our body but to have it in the best possible condition so that we can use it to do the works God has prepared for us.

6. We will be more effective as disciples when we pay attention to diet, exercise, and rest.

7. We are urged to offer our bodies to God as living sacrifices, holy and pleasing to Him.

GOING DEEPER

- Think about the amazing ways your body works and the magnificence of the One who created you. Consider all the different parts of your body: your eyes, ears, digestive tract, skin, brain, heart etc. Spend some time thanking Him for your body and that you are "fearfully and wonderfully made" (Psalm 139:14).

- How have you not loved and honored your body? Have you eaten, exercised, and rested too much or too little? What changes do you want to make?

- Consider whether you have made your body into an idol. Have you spent excessive time, money, energy, or thought on how you look?

- Some of us have "temporary tents" that are not as obviously attractive as those of others, and yet to God we are each a unique, beautiful work of art (that's what the Greek word in Ephesians 2:10 means). Have you despised or hated your body for how it looks or functions? Confess that to God and resolve to renew your mind to the truth.

To Die Is Gain

WHAT'S IT ABOUT?

OBJECTIVE:

To help us bring our thinking into line with God's truth on the subjects of anxiety, fear, and death, so that we can live as fruitful disciples.

FOCUS VERSE:

Since the children have flesh and blood, he too shared in their humanity so that by his death he might break the power of him who holds the power of death – that is, the devil – and free those who all their lives were held in slavery by their fear of death. (Hebrews 2:14-15)

WELCOME

We don't generally talk much about death but it is, of course, very much part of life. What is the most positive experience you have had regarding this subject? You may, for example, have seen someone who "died really well", or been positively impacted by a funeral service.

WORSHIP

Praise God for the fact that the moment you received Jesus as your Lord, you received eternal life and your spirit will live forever. It is a gift from a God of love and grace (see John 3:16, John 10:28, 1 John 5:11).

Video length: 33:40
Pause For Thought 1 comes in at 21:12.
Pause For Thought 2 comes in at 31:16.

WORD

Fear And Anxiety

Fear and anxiety are implicated in a whole host of health issues, particularly those affecting the heart, bowels, and skin.

Yet in the Bible both Jesus and Paul tell us plainly not to be anxious and "Do not fear" is the most repeated commandment in the Bible. If God commands us to do something, then by definition it must be possible for us to do it. This means that every command that God gives us in His Word is in effect a promise. When He says to us, "Do not be anxious about anything," He is *promising* that we don't have to be anxious. When He says to us, "Do not be afraid," implicit in that is a *promise* that it is absolutely possible for us to live without fear.

The difference between fear and anxiety is that fear always has a specific object, for example, snakes, heights, or death. Anxiety on the other hand generates much the same physical reaction as fear but there is no specific cause.

Resolving Anxiety

Jesus said, "Do not be anxious about tomorrow" (Matthew 6:34 ESV). Anxiety is a vague sense of not knowing what is going to happen tomorrow and letting that niggle away at us. We could define it more precisely as: **"the painful and disturbing unease that comes from inappropriate concern about something uncertain."** [1]

Not all concern is inappropriate. It's normal to be nervous about an exam you're about to take or if you're running late for a flight. That anxiety arises from a particular situation and fades away when it's over. It's when anxiety becomes an ongoing, regular part of life that it becomes a problem.

> Humble yourselves, therefore, under the mighty hand of God so that at the proper time he may exalt you, casting all your anxieties on him, because he cares for you. Be sober-minded; be watchful. Your adversary the devil prowls around like a roaring lion, seeking someone to devour. (1 Peter 5:6-8 ESV)

Peter quite clearly links not casting your anxieties onto God with the reality that Satan is prowling around looking for someone to devour. Anxiety poses a spiritual as well as a physical danger.

He specifies two things to do: humble yourself, and cast all your anxieties onto God.

---

1 This definition is taken from *Freed To Lead* by Rod Woods and Steve Goss (Monarch, 2017) and the teaching in this section on fear and anxiety is adapted from it and from Neil Anderson's teaching (see page 192 for further information on *Freed To Lead*).

Humbling Ourselves

Part of humbling ourselves under God's mighty hand is about letting go of our own agenda for our lives.

What long-term goals do you have regarding your health:
- To live a long healthy life?
- To be physically fit?
- To be healed?

What other kinds of long-term goals do you have in life:
- To have a certain level of financial security?
- To have children who serve God and live fruitful lives?
- To rise to a certain position in your career?

It's not wrong to aim for those things. But there is a problem if they cross a line from being just something that we would *like* to see happen in an ideal world to becoming a "life-goal", an objective that has become so important to us that we measure our very success as a person against it.

The problem is that you can't guarantee that any of those goals will be fulfilled. Even if you are physically healthy right now, you don't know what will happen tomorrow. Ultimately you won't be able to control the choices your kids make.

Feeling continually anxious is a strong indication that you may be working towards a life-goal that feels uncertain, in other words, one whose fulfilment depends on people or circumstances that are not within your power to control.

And that means that it's not a goal that God has for you. Would God ever say, "I have a goal for you. I know you may not be able to fulfill it, but try anyway." Of course not! If a goal you have really is from God, there's nothing uncertain about it. If you don't want to be anxious, let go of any goal that can be blocked by other people or circumstances that you have no right or ability to control.

That doesn't mean that we stop working towards things that are clearly good. It's just a question of downgrading the significance of those things in our thinking, so that they are no longer *life-goals* upon which our whole sense of who we are depends but are simply *desires*, things we would love to see happen. If they don't happen, it's disappointing but it's OK.

Adopting God's Goal For Our Lives

The key here is understanding what God's actual goal for our life is and making that our life-goal. Above everything else, God wants you to become more and more like Jesus in character. He is concerned about what you *do* but He is much more concerned about what you are *like*. Because what you do comes from what you are like. He is concerned about what He can do *through* you. But He is more concerned about what He can do *in* you.

Nobody and nothing can block that goal – difficult people and difficult circumstances such as a health problem can actually help you become more like Jesus as you persevere through and grow in character.

In fact the only person who can block God's goal for your life is... you!

Casting Our Anxiety Onto Jesus

Then we are to cast our anxiety onto Jesus. Let's look at a way to do that.

First, in a difficult situation separate the facts from the assumptions. A fact might be something like "I have found a strange lump." An assumption would be, "I have cancer and I am going to die next week!"

Ask yourself, "What here do I have the right or ability to control, and what is beyond my power to control?" You can't do anything about the fact that there is a lump. But you can control what you choose to think and believe.

Then consider, "What in this situation is my responsibility?" It would be sensible, for example, to see a doctor and to go through *The Steps To Freedom In Christ* to check that there is no spiritual issue at the root of this.

Now that you have fulfilled your responsibility, you can confidently say, "Over to you, God," and leave everything else with Him. The principle is: do what is yours to do; then leave the rest to God.

Dealing With Fear

We could define fear as **"an emotional reaction caused by a perceived danger or threat that triggers a physical response in our bodies."** There is healthy fear and unhealthy fear. The difference between the two is essentially about truth and lies – whether or not the danger you *perceive* really is a danger.

Healthy fear stops us doing things that would harm us. For example, you don't put your hand in a fire or play with a lion.

But then there is also unhealthy fear. That is fear that is not a reasonable response to what is happening, e.g., being paralyzed by a small spider in the corner of the room, thinking we are going to get ill at any moment, or sleeping with the light on because of fear of the dark.

For a fear to be healthy it has to have two attributes: it has to be both **present** and **powerful**.

Every unhealthy fear comes from believing that an object is both present and powerful when it isn't. So behind every unhealthy fear is a lie. It's knowing the truth that will set you free from fear.

Most unhealthy fears are related to the fear of other people, or the fear of death.

Fear Of People

Let's say you've got a huge fear of your boss. He's an intimidating kind of person but you are not afraid of him when you are at home. Why not? He's not there. But when you go to work on Monday morning, there he is. Present and powerful.

Or is he? Because the Bible tells us not to fear people. So what can you do to stop the boss producing that kind of fear in you? You have to get rid of one of those attributes. You can't do anything about the fact that he's present. So what about powerful? Well, exactly what power does he have over you? What is the worst thing he could do? He could fire you.

Resolve right now that, if push comes to shove, and your boss starts demanding that you do things that morally you know aren't right, then you will choose to obey God rather than him. Yes, he may fire you, but the truth is that you can trust God to take care of you.

God doesn't want us to remove ourselves from being around other people, so the threat of being rejected by them is always present. Is it powerful? That depends on you! By resolving in your own mind today that, if push comes to shove, you will always obey God rather than people and take His opinion of you rather than theirs, you remove their power. So you do not need to fear them.

PAUSE FOR THOUGHT 1

What are your thoughts on the idea that God's main goal for your life is that you become more and more like Jesus in character?

If you adopted that goal for your life, what difference might it make to you if you found yourself facing a difficult situation such as a health issue or the loss of a job?

Fear Of Death

Different worldviews handle death very differently. Some see it in a very spiritual way, as a joining with the ancestors in the spiritual realm. In the West, there tends to be a physical, non-spiritual approach. Death might be seen as some sort of failure: of the knowledge of the doctors, the care of the health team or our bodies to function as they should. Christians may feel it is a failure of God to answer prayer.

Our natural survival instinct tends to make us fear death and want to avoid it, and Satan is keen to encourage that fear.

However, Hebrews 2:14-15 says that Christ died so that, "by his death he might break the power of him who holds the power of death – that is, the devil – and free those who all their lives were held in slavery by their fear of death." Just as we don't have to be slaves to sin any more, neither do we have to be slaves to the fear of death.

We can't remove the *presence* of death. Unless Jesus comes back first, the one thing in life we can be 100% sure of is that our physical body will die.

But what about death's other attribute, its power? Paul says that death has "lost its sting" (1 Corinthians 15:54-57). Its power has been removed, and so we do not need to fear. Let's look at the truth about death.

We will not all sleep, but we will all be changed – in a flash, in the twinkling of an eye, at the last trumpet. For the trumpet will sound, the dead will be raised imperishable, and we will be changed. (1 Corinthians 15:51-52)

On one level we don't know what's going to happen tomorrow. On another level we know exactly what's going to happen:

- God is going to continue to be our loving, protective Father;
- When we are weak, He will always be strong and we will be able to do all things through Christ who will give us strength (2 Corinthians 12:9-10, Philippians 4:13);
- When our physical body dies, our spirit is still connected to God and we will be with Him for ever in a place where the Bible promises there will be "no more death or mourning or crying or pain" (Revelation 21:4).

Knowing these things in our heart (not just our head) will transform us and enable us to think about our own physical death and – without being morbid – live in the light of it. The Apostle Paul did just that. When he was in prison in Rome with the likelihood of a death sentence coming his way, he wrote this to the Philippians:

It is my eager expectation and hope that I will not be at all ashamed, but that with full courage now as always Christ will be honored in my body, whether by life or by death. For to me to live is Christ, and to die is gain. If I am to live in the flesh, that means fruitful labor for me. Yet which I shall choose I cannot tell. I am hard pressed between the two. (Philippians 1:20-23a ESV)

Paul is torn between staying in the temporary tent of his body and leaving for the joys of heaven. But whether he lives or dies, he wants Christ to be honored in his body. He has made his body a "living sacrifice".

The reason he gives for staying physically alive is that it will mean fruitful labor. He will be able to do more of the things God prepared specifically for him to do.

The bottom line is this: "For to me to live is Christ, and to die is gain." Nothing else works in that equation… "For me to live is my family or my career or my ministry, to die is loss." But when living here in this body is all about Christ and becoming more and more like Him, when we die and get to be with Him, things just get better!

At the end of his last Narnia book, CS Lewis describes heaven like this:

> The things that began to happen after that were so great and beautiful that I cannot write them. All their life in this world had only been the cover and the title page: now at last they were beginning Chapter One of the Great Story which no one on earth has read: which goes on forever: in which every chapter is better than the one before.[2]

Practical Steps To Address Fear

1. Deal with sin issues.

After Adam sinned he said "I was afraid." The sin opened the door to fear. As always, the first step is to confess and repent by going through *The Steps to Freedom in Christ*.

2. Recognize that God is always present AND always powerful.

This is why the fear of God is the one fear that is always healthy. Fear of God doesn't mean being afraid of Him. It means recognizing His power and authority, His holiness and love, and remembering that He is on our side!

3. Work out the lie behind the unhealthy fear.

For example, if I fear Satan, it means I think he is more powerful than I am. The Bible is our "lie detector" and tells us in James 4:7 that if we submit to God and resist the devil, he has to flee from us.

4. Renew your mind using Stronghold-Busting (see page 53).

2 C. S. Lewis, *The Last Battle* (HarperCollins: New York, 1956) p. 228.

PAUSE FOR THOUGHT 2

"Death is still *present* but for us it is no longer *powerful* so need not be feared."
What do you feel about this statement?

What practical things might we do in order to resolve our natural fear of death?

Keys To Take Home

1. **We can resolve anxiety by humbling ourselves before God and casting our cares onto Him.**

2. **We need to let go of any life-goal that can be blocked by circumstances or other people.**

3. **Aligning our goals in life with God's goal for us – to become more and more like Jesus – removes a lot of anxiety.**

4. **For a fear to be healthy, it must be both PRESENT and POWERFUL.**

5. **Behind every unhealthy fear is a lie, and we can resolve the fear by renewing our mind to the truth.**

6. **Death is still PRESENT, but for us it is no longer POWERFUL, so it need not be feared.**

7. **If for me to live is Christ, then when I die it just gets better!**

 GOING DEEPER

All of us are working towards particular life-goals that we have developed.
However, we may not actually know what they are because we develop them sub-
consciously. Take some time to pray and think about the things you are working
towards in your life. Ask God to make you aware of them and write them down.
Then, for each of the goals you identify, ask yourself whether the goal could be

blocked by people or circumstances outside your control. If it can, take some time before God to discern whether or not this goal has not become so important to you that you measure your own success as a person against it. What steps will you take to downgrade it in your thinking?

Consider the certainty of your physical death. How does the thought of death make you feel? Could there be a lie you have believed? Are there events in your life that have molded your view of death in an unhealthy way?

Consider the following verses about what will happen to you when you die:

Listen, I tell you a mystery: We will not all sleep, but we will all be changed – in a flash, in the twinkling of an eye, at the last trumpet. For the trumpet will sound, the dead will be raised imperishable, and we will be changed. (1 Corinthians 15:51-52)

Then I saw "a new heaven and a new earth," for the first heaven and the first earth had passed away. (Revelation 21:1)

And I heard a loud voice from the throne saying, "Behold, the dwelling place of God is with man. He will dwell with them, and they will be his people, and God himself will be with them as their God. He will wipe away every tear from their eyes, and death shall be no more, neither shall there be mourning, nor crying, nor pain anymore, for the former things have passed away."
(Revelation 21:3-4 ESV)

Therefore my heart is glad and my tongue rejoices; my body also will rest secure, because you will not abandon me to the realm of the dead, nor will you let your faithful one see decay. You make known to me the path of life; you will fill me with joy in your presence, with eternal pleasures at your right hand. (Psalm 16:9-11)

What can you do to start bringing your beliefs about death into line with what is actually true?

Will God Heal Me?

WHAT'S IT ABOUT?

OBJECTIVE:

To consider what it means to be truly whole.

To understand how to approach health issues that arise in our lives.

FOCUS VERSE:

You did not choose me, but I chose you and appointed you so that you might go and bear fruit – fruit that will last – and so that whatever you ask in my name the Father will give you. (John 15:16)

 **WELCOME**

What are the key things that have struck you so far on this course?

 WORSHIP

Spend time focusing on these attributes of God:

- the compassion, love, and faithfulness of Father God (Psalm 86:15)
- the name of Jesus, which means "God saves" (Philippians 2:10)
- the hope and power of the Holy Spirit (Romans 15:13).

Video length: 34:29

Pause For Thought 1 comes in at 15:06.

Pause For Thought 2 comes in at 31:50.

WORD

God set up the scientific laws of physics and biology, but has made a habit of intervening in them. Jesus healed all who came to him (Matthew 12:15, Luke 4:40, Luke 6:19); and Paul and the other apostles performed many healing miracles (Acts 5:16, 19:11-12).

On the other hand, it's clear that Jesus saw many people who were suffering but did not heal them. At the pool of Bethesda (John 5:2-9), there was a multitude of invalids – "blind, lame, and paralyzed" – and Jesus healed just one of them. Paul himself was not free from physical illness: "As you know, it was because of an illness that I first preached the gospel to you" (Galatians 4:13). He advised Timothy to take a little wine for his stomach problems and "frequent illnesses" (1 Timothy 5:23). He also said that Trophimus was unable to travel due to illness (2 Timothy 4:20), and that Epaphroditus was so ill that he nearly died (Philippians 2:27). Physical illness was a normal part of life for Christians then as it is now.

Nowhere in the Bible do we learn that we can expect to be healed of every illness *right now*. Illnesses caused by purely physical issues are an inevitable consequence of living in a fallen world in bodies that are dying.

Yet the exact same power that raised Jesus from the dead is in you and me (Ephesians 1:19-20) and Jesus told us that we will do greater works than He did (John 14:12). Also, Paul talked about people with specific "gifts of healing" as a normal part of church life (1 Corinthians 12: 9, 28).

Living Well With A Chronic Illness

If you have done what God gives you to do, and you are still not healed, God is still God and you are still His beloved child. You don't need to be physically healthy to be used powerfully by God. You can be fruitful even with a chronic illness.

Know your true identity in Christ

Our value isn't dependent on what we look like, what we can do, or what others expect. Our value is based purely on who God says we are.

So don't define yourself by illness or say things like "*my* condition, *my* arthritis, *my* heart problems" which imply you somehow *own* the illness.

Make practical changes

We may need to learn to pace ourselves and say no to some things.

Look for positives in all situations

Focus on what you *can* do rather than what you can't do. Learning new skills or hobbies can help. The Bible tells us to give thanks in all circumstances (1 Thessalonians 5:18).

Wholeness And Healing Are Different Things

The key point is this: wholeness is different to healing. Sometimes we can be so insistent on pursuing physical healing that we miss the more important thing.

> Therefore, in order to keep me from becoming conceited, I was given a thorn in my flesh, a messenger of Satan, to torment me. Three times I pleaded with the Lord to take it away from me. But he said to me, "My grace is sufficient for you, for my power is made perfect in weakness." Therefore I will boast all the more gladly about my weaknesses, so that Christ's power may rest on me. That is why, for Christ's sake, I delight in weaknesses, in insults, in hardships, in persecutions, in difficulties. For when I am weak, then I am strong.
> (2 Corinthians 12:7-10)

We are not told exactly what the thorn in the flesh was, other than it was a messenger of Satan, but it was something that made Paul feel very weak. He was right to do everything he could to be free from it. But it didn't happen and God said clearly: "My grace is sufficient for you, for my power is made perfect in weakness."

God's goal for us is to help us become more and more like Jesus in character. Persevering through a difficult health issue and discovering that His grace really is sufficient can really help us in that. Joni Eareckson Tada has spent 50 years in a wheelchair, after being left quadriplegic in a diving accident aged 17. She travels all around the world inspiring thousands of people. She wrote, "My wheelchair was the key to seeing all this happen – especially since God's power always shows up best in weakness. So here I sit ... glad that I have not been healed on the outside, but glad that I have been healed on the inside. Healed from my own self-centered wants and wishes."[1]

Paul assures us that in every circumstance God is working for our good (Romans 8:28). We can be physically *healed* but not *whole*. And we can be increasingly whole yet still have a physical health issue.

---

1 Joni Eareckson Tada, *A Place of Healing: Wrestling with the Mysteries of Suffering, Pain, and God's Sovereignty*, p.49, David C Cook Publishing Company, 2010.

PAUSE FOR THOUGHT 1

"Wholeness is different to healing." In what way could someone be healed but not whole? And whole but not healed?
How would you define "wholeness"?

Answering The Key Question

So, what *does* it mean to be a spiritually alive child of God living in an unredeemed, unrestored world? Let's attempt at last to give this crucial question a complete spirit, mind, and body answer.

The effects of the Fall (Adam's original sin) on our *spirit* have been completely reversed already. Our spirit – the core part of our being – has come back to life and is even now united with God's Spirit.

The effects of the Fall on our *mind, emotions, and will* can now potentially be reversed. The extent to which they are reversed, however, depends on how much we co-operate with God by choosing to walk by the Spirit rather than the flesh, choosing to believe the truth, making good choices, and being transformed by the renewing of our minds.

However, for now we still have the same old physical *body* – and it is getting older all the time. We will one day get a brand new body and sickness will be no more but, until that day comes, we will, "groan inwardly as we wait eagerly for adoption as sons, the redemption of our bodies" (Romans 8:23 ESV).

Transformation in our *spirit* and *mind*, however, should normally lead to positive effects in our physical *body*. If we make a long-term commitment to self-control in things like exercise, eating, and rest, we can expect to reap benefits in our physical health.

An 8-Point Plan To Ensure You Have Done Everything You Can Do

If you have taken medical advice but still have a sickness that has not gone away, we have put together an 8-point plan based on what we've looked at in *Keys To Health, Wholeness, & Fruitfulness*. It will enable you to know that you have done everything within your power and responsibility.

1. Get radically right with God

If you have a problem in your body, it's often impossible to judge immediately whether the root is spiritual, mental, emotional, or purely physical. But you can easily use *The Steps to Freedom in Christ* to resolve or rule out a spiritual cause and we'd recommend you start with that.

2. Follow the instructions in James 5

James 5 has some very specific instructions on what to do if you are sick and a firm promise that you will be healed if you do them:

> Is any one of you in trouble? He should pray. Is anyone happy? Let him sing songs of praise. Is any one of you sick? He should call the elders of the church to pray over him and anoint him with oil in the name of the Lord. And the prayer offered in faith will make the sick person well; the Lord will raise him up. If he has sinned, he will be forgiven. Therefore confess your sins to each other and pray for each other so that you may be healed. The prayer of a righteous man is powerful and effective. (James 5:13-16)

The passage gives the person who is sick a lot of responsibility. *They* are to call the elders. *They* are to pray. There's this command too: "Therefore confess your sins to each other and pray for each other so that you may be healed. The prayer of a righteous man is powerful and effective." Once the sick person has confessed sin, when others pray for them there is healing.

As we've seen, unresolved sin open doors to the enemy's influence and is one possible root of sickness. It's important to rule out that possibility. When you have done your part – confessed your sins – then, if the problem remains, ask the elders of your church to pray for you and anoint you with oil as James suggests. We would expect any issue with a spiritual root to disappear at that point.

Don't go straight to the elders for prayer – do your part first. If the illness continues, it would be reasonable to assume that the root issue is not spiritual.

3. Commit yourself to believing the truth and renewing your mind

We've seen examples of how changing a faulty belief has led to healing of physical symptoms and we've noted that knowing the truth is crucial.

Stronghold-Busting will help you renew your mind which will bring transformation.

Simply declaring out truth from God's Word can help significantly.

4. Seek out someone with a genuine gift of healing

If you can identify a Christian with a genuine gift of healing, ideally in your own church, then ask them to pray for you. But don't feel the need to chase all over the place looking for the right "anointed person".

Beware of charlatans or those who imply they are Christian but who are actually trying to tap into occult powers (such as so-called spiritualist churches).

Be wise about so-called "alternative" healing practices. Some of them are based on spiritual practices from other religions and might open you up to negative spiritual influences. To explore how to judge whether a particular alternative practice is likely to help you or harm you, see *The Biblical Guide To Alternative Medicine* by Neil T. Anderson and Michael Jacobsen (Regal Books, 2003).

5. Do everything you can to look after your body

Ensure you have a good diet, recommended minimum physical activity, and rest. That will require a commitment to walking by the Spirit and letting the fruit of self-control keep growing in your life.

6. See a medical doctor

We're assuming you will have already seen a medical doctor by this point but it might be worth pursuing that path again. Don't think that it is somehow "unspiritual" to seek medical help.

7. Be part of a loving community

Loneliness in the elderly is as big a killer as heart disease.[2] God has designed us to have fellowship with one another. Commit yourself to a body of believers and, if you can, to a small group who will pray with you.

8. Entrust yourself to God and His perfect wisdom

God is God. He loves you. He has perfect wisdom. You are safe in His hands. There is more than a little mystery in all this but, even if you were healed today, the process of decay of your body would continue and (if Jesus doesn't return first) you will eventually die of something else. He can work through you mightily just as you are!

2 *Loneliness and Social Isolation as Risk Factors for Mortality: A Meta-Analytic Review,* Julianne Holt-Lunstad, Timothy B. Smith, Mark Baker, Tyler Harris, and David Stephenson, Brigham Young University, 2015.

Don't Forget!

> Therefore, I urge you, brothers and sisters, in view of God's mercy, to offer your bodies as a living sacrifice, holy and pleasing to God – this is your true and proper worship. Do not conform to the pattern of this world, but be transformed by the renewing of your mind. (Romans 12:1-2a)

You are so much more than your physical body which is just temporary accommodation on earth for your spirit, the part of you that will go on for ever.

Don't let the world dictate how you think. Ruthlessly capture every thought, uncover faulty beliefs, and exchange them for what is actually true.

Remember just who you are and that God created you, chose you, and planned hugely significant things for you to do.

In preparation for that, His focus right now is to help you become more and more like Jesus, to be whole and fruitful.

Fan into flame the gift of the Holy Spirit within you and go out and live for Him!

Keys To Take Home

1. A chronic illness does not in any way prevent you being a whole, fruitful disciple. In fact it can help you towards that.

2. Nevertheless, nothing is impossible for God and He is still in the business of supernatural healing.

3. We are not defined by any illness or limitation but by what our Heavenly Father says about us.

4. There are Biblical steps we can take to try to resolve a health issue, depending on its root cause.

5. We need to play our part and make sure we have done the things that God has given us the responsibility to do.

6. We really can learn to give thanks in all circumstances.

7. After we have done all we can do, then we simply entrust our bodies to God as living sacrifices, confident that He can still use us fully as disciples.

PAUSE FOR THOUGHT 2

Taking into account what we have looked at concerning body, mind, and spirit roots of illness, what course of action would you suggest to someone who has recently been diagnosed with a serious illness?

GOING DEEPER

Spend some time reading these verses slowly and asking God to speak to you from them before considering the questions that follow:

> Therefore, I urge you, brothers and sisters, in view of God's mercy, to offer your bodies as a living sacrifice, holy and pleasing to God – this is your true and proper worship. Do not conform to the pattern of this world, but be transformed by the renewing of your mind. (Romans 12:1-2)

> Dear friend, I pray that you may enjoy good health and that all may go well with you, even as your soul is getting along well. (3 John 2)

Is it your inner person or your outer person that matters more to God? Which matters more to you?

How are you growing more like Jesus in character and fruitfulness? Are there any areas of your life in which you would like to grow more? Tell God about them.

If you have a chronic health condition, consider these questions:
* How can my condition help me towards being a fruitful disciple?
* Am I taking responsibility for the things that are mine to do, such as confess, repent, forgive, and speak the truth about who I am in Christ?
* Am I letting go of the things that are not mine to do, such as heal, and provide?
* Am I radically right with God?
* Am I renewing my mind to the truth?
* Have I asked for prayer and anointing with oil for healing?
* Am I choosing to be joyful always, praying continually, and giving thanks in all circumstances?

FREEDOM IN CHRIST

The Steps To Healing And Wholeness

Introduction

The Steps To Healing And Wholeness is the ministry component of *Keys To Health, Wholeness, And Fruitfulness*, and will help you put into practice the principles that have been taught. It is designed specifically for those who want to:

- make sure that their thinking about health is in line with God's Word;
- address a particular health issue from a spirit-mind-body perspective;
- simply take some time to offer themselves to God as a living sacrifice and commit to being the person He is calling them to be, and to do the things He has prepared in advance for them to do.

The Steps To Healing And Wholeness is a tool that will help you:

1. Close any doors in your life that have been opened to the enemy through past sin so that you can remove any influence he may have.
2. Allow the Holy Spirit to show you areas of your belief system that are not in line with what is actually true according to God's Word, so that you can take steps to renew your mind. This, according to the Bible (Romans 12:2), is how you will be transformed.

It is designed to be used as a follow-up to *The Steps To Freedom in Christ* by Dr. Neil T. Anderson. If you have not been through *The Steps To Freedom in Christ* recently, our suggestion is that, if you can, you do that first. It is a more comprehensive process that covers a range of fundamental issues.

If You Have A Specific Health Issue

We are whole people – spirit, mind, and body. When we consider the cause of a particular health issue, we need to take the whole of reality into account. This process will help you do that.

If a Christian has a condition caused by a *spiritual* issue (a foothold of the enemy), they can have every expectation that it can be completely resolved as they choose to submit to God and resist the devil during this process. If the root of the condition is a *mind* issue, a faulty belief, they can have confidence that the Holy Spirit will reveal that during this process. They can then work to change that belief, to renew their mind, and can expect to see transformation, over time, as they bring their belief system into line with the truth of God's Word. If a Christian has a condition caused purely by a *physical* issue, they can be assured that their body is just a "temporary tent" and that they will get a perfect new body in the future. They can also be assured that God will use the difficulties they face to deepen their character – and godly character is His primary goal for our lives. Over and above that, they can seek prayer and ask God for a miracle, knowing that He is perfectly capable of healing instantly even the most serious physical illness. The exact same power that raised Christ from the dead is in you and me and Jesus told us that we would do greater works than He did!

We would encourage you not to come into this process looking primarily for physical healing (though that may come). Being physically healthy is not a good enough objective in itself. Come simply to ensure that you have done everything that is within your power and responsibility, and then entrust yourself to God's mercy and wisdom, knowing that He loves you so much and has specific things for you to do. He will enable you to do them regardless of whether you are perfectly physically healthy or not.

Seek Medical Help Too

Some Christians have been taught that seeking medical help is somehow "unspiritual" or demonstrates a lack of faith in God. It is neither of those things but is an eminently sensible course of action. Medical professionals are part of God's provision for our health.

This process is not an alternative to consulting a medical doctor. If you have a health issue, do not delay in seeking medical advice.

How To Use *The Steps To Healing And Wholeness*

The Steps To Healing And Wholeness is designed to be run under the auspices of a local church and we strongly recommend you use it in that context. It can be used by a group on an "away day" or in an individual one-to-one appointment, ideally with a prayer partner also in attendance. We recommend that churches take care to ensure that the process is led by people approved by them and in accordance with its protection policies.

The process is self-explanatory. Speak the prayers in bold text out loud and take as much time as you need to consider the areas you need to deal with.

If you are using the accompanying video to guide you through the process, pause the video when you see the "Pause For Prayer" graphic come up and press "Play" when you are ready to continue. The video is one hour and ten minutes in length.

Going Through As A Group On An Away Day

It is recommended that you hold the away day in pleasant surroundings, away from your church if possible. Aim to provide lunch or make sure that people bring their own. The room you use should be large enough for participants to have some degree of privacy. It is helpful if people can spread out. It may help to have some music playing in the background during the prayer times so that people can pray out loud without feeling that others are listening. Instrumental music works best as it is less distracting.

Each participant will need a copy of this book and a pencil or pen. The group will be praying several prayers together out loud. Then they will spend some time alone with God. Nobody will be embarrassed or asked to share anything with the group or another person. It is solely an encounter with God. We strongly recommend that churches arrange to have suitable people available to pray or talk with individuals if needed.

Some people will have very little to deal with on some steps, whereas others may have a lot. Those who do not have much on a particular step could spend time praying for those who do: that the Holy Spirit will reveal everything that needs to be revealed; and that Satan's attempts to interfere in the process will be ineffective. If you find you have too much to deal with in the time available, this is not a one-off opportunity and you can catch up in your own time. The ideal would be to arrange to go through the process again with an appropriate person leading you in a one-to-one appointment.

Here is a suggested timetable for an away day:

10.00am	Introduction	10 minutes
	(Explain the process and the logistics of the day.)	
10.10am	Opening Prayers and My Story	30 minutes
10.40am	Step 1: My Worldview	15 minutes
10.55am	Step 2: Embracing God's Plan For My Life	10 minutes
11.05am	Step 3: Spiritual Roots	50 minutes
	Living As Though Nothing Has Changed	*10 minutes*
	Reaping What I Sow	*5 minutes*
	Unresolved Personal Sin	*15 minutes*
	Negative Inheritance From My Family Line	20 minutes

11.55am	Step 4: Difficult Past Events	20 minutes
12.15pm	Step 5: Forgiveness	30 minutes
12.45pm	Break	60 minutes
1.45pm	Step 6: Choosing To Be Well	10 minutes
1.55pm	Step 7: Regaining Freedom From Compulsive Behaviors And Addictions	20 minutes
2.15pm	Step 8: The Temple Of The Holy Spirit	15 minutes
2.30pm	Step 9: Anxiety And Fear	60 minutes
	Humbling Ourselves By Adopting God's Goal For Our Lives	*20 minutes*
	Casting Anxiety Onto Jesus	*20 minutes*
	Fear	*20 minutes*
3.30pm	Step 10: Facing Chronic Illness	10 minutes
3.40pm	Closing Prayer	5 minutes
3.45pm	Calling The Elders	30 minutes
4.15pm	Renewing Your Mind (This will not include time to write a Stronghold-Buster, just time to identify lies.)	15 minutes
4.30pm	Finish	

At The End Of The Process

In James 5:13-16, the person who is sick is given a great deal of responsibility. They have to pray, they have to take the initiative, and they have to confess sin. Then, when others pray for them, there is healing. Therefore, at the end of this process, we have included a section entitled "Calling The Elders" (page 175) where those who have been praying and confessing can ask leaders from their church to anoint them with oil if they have a specific health issue.

We have not laid down any instructions or given specific prayers to use but suggest that leaders carry out a simple process of anointing according to the traditions of their particular church. There is no need to prolong this time. Simply anoint people and spend some time praying for their healing.

If the process has been carried out as a one-to-one appointment or in some other context where an elder is not present, we would encourage participants to request that an elder from their church meets with them on a different occasion specifically to anoint them and pray for their healing.

Opening Prayers

Begin by speaking the following prayer out loud.

> Lord God,
>
> You are the Creator of all things. You are the one true God. You alone know the end from the beginning. There is none like You.
>
> I come humbly before You this day. Thank You for freely welcoming me into Your presence.
>
> I affirm that Jesus Christ is my Lord, and that everything I am and have belongs to You. My desire is to be the person You are calling me to be and to do the things that You have prepared in advance for me to do.
>
> You have promised to give wisdom to those who ask You for it. I humbly ask You to give me wisdom today and reveal to me everything You want me to know, particularly about my health, wholeness, and fruitfulness.
>
> Please show me all the areas in my life where I have allowed the enemy a foothold, in order that I may turn away from my sin and remove any influence he may have.
>
> I ask Your Holy Spirit to lead me into all truth and to show me where my belief system is not in line with what is actually true according to Your Word, so that I may renew my mind to the truth.
>
> I pray this in the name of Jesus, who died for my wholeness and rose again to give me life in all its fullness.
>
> Amen.

Specific Health Issues

Are there specific health issues that you wish to bring before God during this time? List them below and then pray the prayer that follows:

Lord God,

I specifically bring before You _____ [list the health issue(s)].

I pray that during this time You will reveal to me the root causes, whether spiritual, mental, or physical, and give me the strength to deal with those that are within my area of responsibility.

My desire is for healing and I humbly ask You for that. But my greatest desire, Father, is to be a fruitful disciple of Jesus who is used mightily by You. I commit my whole self, including my physical body, into Your hands and I choose to trust You regarding whether I am healed or not.

I simply ask that You have Your way in me.

In Jesus' name.

Amen.

My Story

As you begin this time of prayerful reflection, take some time to write down a timeline of your life and give the Holy Spirit an opportunity to highlight certain things that He wants you to deal with during the process.

Lord God,

As I reflect on my life, I pray for Your wisdom. Please guide my thoughts and please begin to help me understand some of the things You want me to address today.

In Jesus' name.

Amen.

Go back as far as you can remember and use the following page to write down the key events in your life, both positive and negative.

If you have particular health issues, what is the story of the illness or the symptoms that you are experiencing? Was there something else that happened at the time an illness started: perhaps a bereavement, trauma, stressful situation, or loss? Think about people who influenced your life positively and negatively at that time.

Key Life Events With Approximate Dates

Include, for example, events such as marriage, birth of children, and divorce, as well as any traumatic events.

Health Issues With Approximate Dates They Began

List major or chronic health issues. Do they coincide with key life events above?

Patterns Of Illness In Your Family

Consider parents, grandparents, and other ancestors as far back as you know and make a list of all illnesses that you know have arisen in your family.

Before moving on, highlight any areas that you feel you particularly need to bring before God during this process. Many of them will come up naturally during the process but it will be worth checking back before you finish to make sure you have covered everything you need to.

Step 1: My Worldview

All of us have learned to see reality in a particular way, influenced by our culture, our education, our family background, our friends, the media we consume, and many other factors. None of us, however, learned to see reality as it actually is, which is why God gives us this instruction:

> Do not conform to the pattern of this world, but be transformed by the renewing of your mind. Then you will be able to test and approve what God's will is – his good, pleasing, and perfect will. (Romans 12:2)

How we see the world depends very much on when and where we were born and raised. In this Step, we will ask the Holy Spirit to help us become aware of faulty beliefs we absorbed as we grew up, so that we can take steps to renew our minds.

> **Lord God,**
>
> **I recognize that I have followed the ways of this world and have developed a set of core beliefs that are not in line with what You tell me in Your Word is actually true.**
>
> **I have had these beliefs for so long, and they are so deeply ingrained, that it is difficult for me to recognize them. I pray that You would reveal to me all my faulty beliefs, in order that I might renew my mind and live according to what is actually true.**
>
> **I recognize that my faulty worldview has influenced the way I have learned to view sickness and healing. Please help me see where I have believed things that are not true.**
>
> **I pray in the name of Jesus who is *the* Truth.**
>
> **Amen.**

There are many different worldviews: every religion or philosophy is a worldview; every culture is based on a particular worldview; every new generation tends to have a worldview that is different to that of preceding generations. We are influenced far more than we tend to realize by our worldviews and we don't always believe what we *say* or *think* we believe. For example, you may say and think that you believe in the power of prayer. If, however, you are not actually praying in any meaningful way day-to-day, it shows that you don't actually believe in it. This may helpfully highlight that the Western worldview has influenced you more than you realize. It is what we *do*, not what we *say*, that shows what we really believe.

Our worldview has a great effect on how we attempt to deal with health issues. Consider your typical course of action when faced with illness in yourself or someone else. Do you turn to spiritual help, physical help, alternative therapy help, to God? What are your choices based on? What your family did? What people in your country or culture do? What the media tells you? Scientific data? Consider whether the choices you make are in agreement with how God says the world actually works.

Listed below are characteristics of three worldviews that are prevalent today, particularly those that may affect our attitude to health. Take time to allow the Holy Spirit to show you how you have been influenced by faulty worldviews and mark any attitudes that you recognize in yourself (from any of the worldviews listed).

The Animistic Worldview

The animistic worldview sees the world as controlled by a kind of universal power that runs through everything – animals, plants, and minerals – and by spirits or gods of many kinds. It is found throughout the world but particularly in Africa and Asia, and elements of it are found in many non-Christian religions. Attitudes typical of the animistic worldview include:

- ❏ Being overly concerned that others may have put a curse on me, my family, my finances, or my health.
- ❏ Feeling that I have no control or authority over spiritual powers and need to call in an expert or "anointed" person to sort them out for me.
- ❏ Refusing to consult or listen to the advice of doctors in favor of seeking a "spiritual" remedy.
- ❏ Thinking that medical wisdom is irrelevant and that all sickness is caused by spiritual issues.
- ❏ Thinking that God caused my illness as punishment.
- ❏ Seeking physical health and wealth above everything else.

The Western Or "Modern" Worldview

You are likely to have been influenced to some extent by the Western or "modern" worldview if you were raised in, or live in, the West or received a Western education. The older you are, the more significant this is likely to be in your thinking. It is characterized by so-called "rational" thinking and a reliance on what can be seen, touched, and tested.

Attitudes typical of the Western or "modern" worldview include:

- ☐ Finding it difficult to believe that the spiritual beings the Bible describes – such as angels and demons – are real, or living as though the spiritual world is not relevant in daily life.
- ☐ Paying lip service to the power of prayer but living in practice as if it's my own efforts that count.
- ☐ Saying I believe God's Word but in practice considering my medical or scientific training to be superior where the two appear to conflict.
- ☐ Believing that what medical professionals say is more significant than what God says.
- ☐ Thinking that medication or some other physical intervention is always the answer to physical illness and so being unwilling to consider that there may be deeper roots.
- ☐ Not being willing to address possible spiritual issues in my life in a meaningful way.

The "Postmodern" Worldview

You are likely to have been influenced to some extent by the "postmodern" worldview if you were raised in, or live in, the West or received a "Western" education. The younger you are, the more significant this is likely to be in your thinking. It is characterized by a sense that there is no absolute truth.

Beliefs typical of the postmodern worldview:
- ☐ Believing that there are many different truths, all of which are equally valid.
- ☐ Thinking that there are no real consequences for people who choose not to accept Jesus' free gift of eternal life.
- ☐ Having a tendency to emphasize God's love and forgiveness but de-emphasize His other characteristics, such as holiness and righteousness.
- ☐ Pursuing physical health and "happiness" more than pursuing God and His ways.
- ☐ Turning to non-Christian religions or faith healers who attempt to access a source of spiritual healing other than Jesus (e.g., Reiki, hypnosis, crystals, yoga, spiritualism).

Other Worldviews

List any other worldviews, such as non-Christian religions and philosophies, that you have believed, together with any specific lies or wrong attitudes you picked up from them:

Use the following prayer to begin to turn away from the wrong ways of thinking you have marked:

Father God,

Thank You that You have revealed in the Bible what is true and that it is knowing the truth that sets me free.

I choose now to throw off the faulty ways in which I learned to see the world. I specifically turn away from the lies I have believed in these areas: _____ [list the items you have marked].

From now on, I choose to believe the truth that the Bible is Your message to the people You created, to make it the foundation of my life, and to renew my mind to the truth it contains.

In the name of Jesus.

Amen.

Step 2: Embracing God's Plan For My Life

Take some time to read these verses through slowly and consider them before moving on to the prayer:

> Your eyes saw my unformed body; all the days ordained for me were written in your book before one of them came to be. (Psalm 139:16)

> For we are God's handiwork, created in Christ Jesus to do good works, which God prepared in advance for us to do. (Ephesians 2:10)

Father,

Thank You that I am not an accident and that You laid out the days of my life before I was even born. Thank You that You have a purpose for my life and specific things for me to do, which You have prepared in advance. Please show me now where I have not lived in accordance with this amazing fact.

Amen.

Consider the following actions and attitudes and mark any that you recognize in yourself:

- ❑ Not believing that God has a specific purpose for my life on earth, or that He has prepared works in advance specifically for me to do.
- ❑ Doing what I want to do rather than embracing the plans God has for me.
- ❑ Relying on my own understanding rather than trusting God with all my heart (Proverbs 3:5).
- ❑ Not believing that God will provide everything I need as I do the things that He has called me to do (see Philippians 4:19).
- ❑ Believing that God has turned His back on me because of past sin, a health issue, or some other reason.

Father God,

I confess that I have been guilty of [name the items you marked]. **Thank You for Your forgiveness.**

I choose from this moment on to seek Your Kingdom and Your righteousness above all else (Matthew 6:33) **and I joyfully accept and embrace the plans You have for me, which are to prosper me and not to harm me** (Jeremiah 29:11). **Amen.**

Step 3: Spiritual Roots

Our spirits are now alive and connected to God. They have been gloriously, wonderfully 100% restored to how they were meant to be! In this Step we are going to cover four areas that might be preventing us from seeing the benefits of this wonderful spiritual connection to our Heavenly Father in our day-to-day lives.

1. Living As Though Nothing Has Changed

The moment we turned to Jesus, we became completely new people (2 Corinthians 5:17). God delights in you and loves you – and that is solely because of His grace, not because of anything you have done.

If you follow Jesus, your identity is not based on your past but on Jesus' past.

However, even though we have now been born into His family and are sons and daughters of the King of Kings Himself – princes and princesses! – it's very easy to retain the mind-set of an orphan, to think that nothing has really changed.

No Longer Orphans

Declare confidently out loud the following truths from the Bible:

> Father God, thank You that You did not leave me as an orphan. Thank You that I can now cry to You, "Abba, Father".
>
> I refuse to believe the lie that I am an orphan.
>
> I choose to believe the truth that I have been born into Your family and am now Your much-loved child.
>
> I refuse to believe the lie that, in order for You to love me, I have to do things to please You.
>
> I choose to believe the truth that You love me just as I am because You are love.
>
> I refuse to believe the lie that I have to strive for Your attention.
>
> I choose to believe the truth that You always give me Your full attention.
>
> I refuse to believe the lie that You will reject me if I don't perform well.
>
> I choose to believe the truth that You accept me completely even when I fail.

I refuse to believe the lie that I have to provide for myself.

I choose to believe the truth that You promise to give me everything I need.

I refuse to believe the lie that I can trust only myself.

I choose to believe the truth that You promise to help me and I can trust You completely.

I refuse to believe the lie that no one really knows me or cares about me.

I choose to believe the truth that You knew me before the creation of the world and that Jesus would have died just for me if I had been the only person who needed Him to.

I refuse to believe the lie that I have to compare myself to others.

I choose to believe the truth that I am unique and that You value and love me for who I am.

I refuse to speak badly of myself.

I choose to speak about myself the same way You speak about me.

I refuse to believe the lie that I deserve punishment or illness.

I choose to believe the truth that Jesus took all the punishment I deserved.

I declare that I want to be whole, well, and fruitful and, by Your grace, that is what I will be.

Amen.

Pause to reflect on what you have just read. What are the top three lies from the list that you have been prone to believe? List them below.

1.

2.

3.

2. Reaping What I Sow

> Do not be deceived: God cannot be mocked. A man reaps what he sows.
> (Galatians 6:7)

Our choices and actions have consequences. God loves us and tells us what is good for us and what is bad for us. If we choose to do what is bad for us, we will face consequences.

Pray the following prayer to take responsibility for your actions and choices:

Father God,

I recognize that, in the way You have chosen to set the world up, my choices and actions have consequences. I confess that I have believed the lie that my choices and actions do not have consequences and have lived accordingly.

Please show me now the areas of my life where I have not taken responsibility for my actions.

In Jesus' name.

Amen

Mark the ways you have not taken responsibility for your choices and actions:

- ☐ Refusing to obey clear guidelines from the Bible.
- ☐ My attitude to money.
- ☐ My attitude to sex.
- ☐ Not being prepared to admit I was wrong.
- ☐ Being unwilling to take advice from others.
- ☐ Being undisciplined in eating, drinking, or exercise and assuming there will be no adverse health consequences.
- ☐ Other: _____

Take responsibility for yourself and your life by praying the following prayer:

> Father God,
>
> I thank You that You have given me free will, the ability to make genuine choices. I confess that I have often used this freedom to make bad choices, especially in these areas: _____. Thank You for Your forgiveness. I now choose to turn away from these sins.
>
> Thank You that You have already given me everything I need to live a godly life (2 Peter 1:3). From now on I choose to take responsibility for my choices and actions, recognizing that they have real consequences in my life and in the lives of other people.
>
> In Jesus' name.
>
> Amen.

3. Unresolved Personal Sin

It's clear from the Bible that sometimes sin leads directly to sickness: Egypt suffered deadly plagues when Pharaoh disobeyed God (Exodus 7:14-11:10); King Uzziah's pride led him into disobedience and the consequence was leprosy (2 Chronicles 26:16-20); Elymas the sorcerer was struck blind when he blatantly opposed God (Acts 13:6-12); sickness in the church in Corinth came from "eating and drinking judgment on themselves" because they were handling the bread and the wine wrongly (1 Corinthians 11:29-30); the church in Thyatira is warned that sickness will come unless they repent of sexual immorality (Revelation 2:22-23).

Ask God to show you where there are any unresolved sin issues in your life, whether or not they have led to sickness, so that you can deal with them today:

> Father,
>
> Please show me now all the areas in my life where I have sinned against You and given ground in my life to the enemy, so that I may turn away from that sin and resist the enemy.
>
> In Jesus' name.
>
> Amen.

List the sins you recognize you have committed:

- ❑ Pride
- ❑ Rebellion (against, for example, civil authorities, parents, teachers, church leaders)
- ❑ Sexual relationships outside marriage
- ❑ Trying to meet my needs apart from God
- ❑ Anger
- ❑ Bitterness and unforgiveness
- ❑ Other: _____

If you have a health issue, take a moment to consider the time it started. Could there be any link with sin?

Lord God,

I confess that I have sinned by _____ (list the sins). I acknowledge that this may have resulted in illness in my body or mind. Thank You for Your forgiveness. I humbly ask You to heal any illness in my body or mind that has come as a result of my sin.

In Jesus' name. Amen.

If you have listed sexual sin, it's important to note Paul's teaching that, if a child of God whose spirit is joined to God's Spirit also joins with a prostitute, they become "one flesh" (1 Corinthians 6:15-17). This is not just a physical bonding – they become spiritually bonded together.

Take a moment to write down the names of all the people with whom you have had sexual relationships outside marriage and pray the following prayer for each one:

Father God,

I confess having sexual relations with _____. I ask You to break that sinful bond right now.

Amen.

The wonderful thing is that, no matter how many past sexual experiences you may have had or what they were, they do not change your new identity as a holy one. You are completely forgiven. You are clean and pure in Christ!

4. Negative Inheritance From My Family Line

We all have a negative inheritance from our parents, grandparents, and other ancestors. We are not guilty for our parents' sin but because all parents sin, there are consequences of their sin that will affect us. This concept of passing sins on from one generation to another is a well-attested social phenomenon: for example, abusers have often themselves been abused.

The debate, of course, in the world is whether this comes from the environment you grew up in or whether it is somehow a vulnerability to a certain sin that is "programmed" into your genes. Both of those things influence us but, even if you have a genetic vulnerability to a particular sin, it is by no means inevitable that you will commit it, because personal choice can override the influence from genes. But this clearly happens at a spiritual level too. There are a number of passages in the Bible that indicate this. Perhaps the most significant one is in the Ten Commandments where God said this:

> "You shall not make for yourself an image in the form of anything in heaven above or on the earth beneath or in the waters below. You shall not bow down to them or worship them; for I, the Lord your God, am a jealous God, punishing the children for the sin of the parents to the third and fourth generation of those who hate me, but showing love to a thousand generations of those who love me and keep my commandments." (Exodus 20:4-6)

The iniquities of one generation can adversely affect future generations unless those sins of the ancestors are confessed and renounced.

This may be a *physical* inheritance passed down through our genes, making us a little more vulnerable to a particular sin.

It may be a *mental* inheritance in terms of customs, practices, and ways of thinking that we have picked up from our environment. If your parents left pornography around the house, for example, you will probably struggle with that issue more than somebody who did not get that kind of exposure. If they modeled negative attitudes such as an unwillingness to take responsibility or an unhealthy lifestyle, you may unthinkingly have adopted those attitudes too.

It may be a *spiritual* inheritance in that their sin can open the door for the enemy to influence not just their lives but the lives of their descendants. Sexual sin and involvement in the occult or secret societies such as Freemasonry in one generation seem particularly to affect subsequent generations.

We don't need to work out whether a particular issue is genetic, mental, or spiritual in order to renounce it and turn away from it. Ask God to show you all the specific negative things you have inherited from your ancestors so that you can stand against them and guard your mind:

Father God,

Thank You for the positive inheritance I have from my parents, grandparents, and other ancestors.

I recognize, however, that I have inherited negative things from them too, and today I choose to take my stand against those, so that, as far as it is within my power, I may put a stop to them.

Please reveal to me now the negative influences that have come to me through my family line.

In Jesus' name.

Amen.

Sins And Wrong Attitudes Of Ancestors

- ❏ Anger
- ❏ Fear
- ❏ Anxiety
- ❏ Depressive thinking
- ❏ Low self-esteem
- ❏ Self-hatred
- ❏ Bitterness and unforgiveness
- ❏ Divisiveness
- ❏ Hopelessness
- ❏ Getting identity from illness
- ❏ Perfectionism
- ❏ Lying
- ❏ Bigotry
- ❏ Pride

- ❏ Defensiveness
- ❏ Occult practices (including Freemasonry)
- ❏ False religions
- ❏ Legalistic religious practices
- ❏ Sexual sin
- ❏ Violence
- ❏ Controlling or manipulating other people
- ❏ Gossip
- ❏ Addictions
- ❏ Other sins and wrong attitudes:
  _____

Sickness Of Ancestors

List any illnesses, diseases, and physical and mental disorders that you think might have been passed down your family line:

Now make this declaration:

> I reject and disown all sins and wrong attitudes committed by my ancestors, including _____ [list the sins and wrong attitudes you have marked]. I take back any ground they gave to the enemy in my family line.
>
> I reject and disown all illnesses, diseases, and physical and mental disorders passed down to me from my ancestors including [list the sicknesses that repeat down the generations].
>
> I command every enemy of the Lord Jesus Christ to leave me and my family.
>
> In Jesus' name.
>
> Amen.

Go back and look at the list of Sins And Wrong Attitudes Of Ancestors again. Put a circle around any of the attitudes or sins that you recognize you are vulnerable to repeating. Now that the spiritual root is dealt with, you can choose to renew your mind using Stronghold-Busting in order to bring your belief system into line with God's Word.

Step 4: Difficult Past Events

All of us have suffered traumatic or difficult events in the past to one degree or another. Often they can continue to exert a negative influence on our thinking many years later unless we choose to put a stop to that. It is crucial that we understand that traumatic events from the past are not in themselves the problem – it's the lies they caused us to believe that stay with us. In order to break free, we need to recognize those lies and choose to bring our belief system into line with what is actually true.

> Lord God,
>
> I joyfully declare the truth that nothing that happened to me in the past changes anything about my new identity in Jesus. Regardless of what I did or what others did to me, I am a holy one. I am clean. You delight in me.
>
> Please bring to my mind now the difficult events from my past that You want me to deal with today. And please help me to understand the faulty beliefs that I have taken from those events so that I can take steps to renew my mind and be transformed.
>
> In Jesus' name.
>
> Amen.

First, simply write down the difficult events from your past that He brings to your mind:

When you are sure that you have listed them all, start to consider how those events made you feel and write those feelings down (e.g., dirty, guilty, shameful, useless, rejected, hopeless, inferior).

Do you still tend to feel that way? Put a circle around the beliefs you intend to change by renewing your mind.

Find a truth from God's Word for each one you have circled and then make the following declaration for each faulty belief that you realize is still affecting you:

Lord God,

I recognize that negative experiences have led me to believe the lie that _____.

I choose no longer to believe that lie but to believe the truth from Your Word that _____.

Amen.

Making this declaration is an important start but it is only a start. It takes time and effort to change the way you have learned to think but imagine how different your life could be if you did not have to live with these faulty beliefs any more. Let that spur you on to use Stronghold-Busting to tear them down (see page 53).

Step 5: Forgiveness

We are told, "Forgive as the Lord forgave you" (Colossians 3:13). God commands you to forgive because He loves you (see 2 Corinthians 2:10-11). Unforgiveness gives the enemy a foothold in your life – a spiritual root that could conceivably be a doorway to illness. It also affects your thinking negatively, another possible root of physical symptoms.

The reason we find it so difficult to forgive someone who has hurt us is because we want to see justice done. Understandably, we want them to pay for what they did. Perhaps we have the impression that, in commanding us to forgive, God is asking us to sweep what was done to us under the carpet, to say in effect that it didn't matter. But, of course, it did matter very much.

What God actually says to us is the very opposite to what we tend to think. Read the following verse carefully:

> Do not take revenge, my dear friends, but leave room for God's wrath, for it is written: "It is mine to avenge; I will repay," says the Lord. (Romans 12:19)

When you forgive, although you are letting the person off your hook, you are not letting them off God's hook. You are taking a step of faith to trust God to be the righteous judge who will make everything right by demanding full payment for everything done against you. Nothing will be swept under the carpet.

Everyone who sinned against you will have to stand before God and explain it – either it will be paid for by the blood of Jesus if the person follows Jesus, or they will have to face the judgment of God if they do not.

So you can make the choice to hand all of that pain and those demands for justice over to God, safe in the knowledge that justice will be done. In the meantime you can walk free of it.

How do we forgive? Jesus says we need to forgive "from the heart" (Matthew 18:35). That means being emotionally honest about what was done to us and just how much it hurt us. We have to face the pain and the hate that we feel. We have to be honest with God.

This is not easy but it is essential. We will continue to suffer spiritual torment, negative emotions, and possibly physical illness until we forgive. We can't move on from the past until we forgive. We won't be able to do what God has prepared for us to do until we forgive. We won't be fruitful disciples until we forgive.

You do it in order to *resolve* this issue and get rid of the pain that you have been carrying around.

Ask God to show you whom you need to forgive:

Father God,

Thank You that You command me to forgive, because You love me and want me to be a fruitful disciple, with nothing holding me back from doing the things You have prepared for me to do.

I ask You to show me now all the people that I need to forgive.

In Jesus' name.

Amen.

Take plenty of time to let the Holy Spirit show you who you need to forgive. Cast your mind back over your life from your earliest memories and simply write down the names that come to your mind. Consider, for example, members of your family, people at school, friends, church leaders, and medical professionals.

Before you move on, consider whether you should add two further names to your list: God and yourself:

Forgiving God

God is perfect and has done nothing wrong. However, forgiveness is primarily about what we *feel* rather than what is objectively true. Have you felt that God has let you down or that He was not there for you? Are you holding God responsible for a particular illness or for not healing a particular health issue?

Forgiving Yourself

God has already forgiven you completely, but do you need to catch up with that and forgive yourself for bad choices you made and wrong things you did? This may be particularly relevant if you are struggling with some of the consequences of those actions.

You may feel that you can't forgive. Recognize that, if God commands you to forgive, then by definition you *can* do it. It's simply a choice you make. Don't wait until you feel like forgiving because that day will never come. Just make the choice to do it – for your own good. For each person on your list, pray the following:

Father God,

I choose to forgive _____ [name] for _____ [what they did or failed to do] **which made me feel _____**[tell God how what they did made you feel].

Jesus tells us to "love your enemies and pray for those who persecute you" (Matthew 5:44). Put that into practice now by praying the following prayer for those on your list who are still alive:

Father,

In the name of Jesus I bless _____ [list all those you have forgiven]. **I pray for those that do not yet know You, that they will turn to You and be saved. I pray for those that do know You, that You will give them fruitful ministries.**
Amen.

Step 6: Choosing To Be Well

On one occasion Jesus came across someone who had been an invalid for 38 years. Before He healed him, He asked him an important question: "Do you want to get well?" (John 5:6).

Being sick can become part of our identity. It can bring us support, love, care, even money, that we may not be willing to give up. The thought of getting better can be quite scary.

It's important to be honest about what we gain from our illness and make a definite decision to want to be well.

> Father God,
> Thank You that You want me to be whole. Thank You that nothing is hidden from You. You know all my thoughts, words, and deeds and yet love me always.
> Please show me now any ways in which I have allowed sickness to become part of my identity and any other ways I may be holding on to it.
> In Jesus' name.
> Amen.

Reasons I may not want to be well:

- ❑ Feeling that sickness gives me a special identity.
- ❑ Believing that I deserve sickness or punishment.
- ❑ Not wanting to give up the attention from others that sickness brings.
- ❑ Not wanting to give up the financial benefits that sickness brings.
- ❑ Fear (of _____).
- ❑ Being unwilling to face change.
- ❑ Other: _____

Pray the following prayer:

> Father God,
>
> I confess that I have not wanted to be well because of
> _____.
>
> Thank You for Your forgiveness. I choose to trust You to provide for all my needs including security, safety, value, identity, purpose, attention, peace, strength, and finances.
>
> I declare now that I do want to be whole and well in spirit, mind, emotions, and body.
>
> I entrust myself to Your wisdom and grace.
>
> In the name of Jesus who died for my wholeness.
>
> Amen.

We may also need to take notice of how we speak about health issues. Do you talk about "my sickness"? Have you ever thought or spoken out negative things about yourself because of a health issue? If so, pray this prayer:

> Lord God,
>
> I confess that I have spoken negatively about myself because of health issues. I confess that I have taken false ownership of illness by considering it as "my" illness. I resolve not to do that any longer.
>
> I give You all disability, illness, pain, and torment that is affecting me and declare the truth that those things do not define who I am. I declare the truth that I am a holy child of the Living God and I choose to speak about myself the same way You speak about me, using words that bring life.
>
> In the name of Jesus.
>
> Amen.

Step 7: Regaining Freedom From Compulsive Behaviors And Addictions

In 1 Corinthians 6:12, some of the Corinthians quote a saying, "I have the right to do anything." Paul doesn't contradict them. He simply says, "But not everything is beneficial. 'I have the right to do anything' – but I will not be mastered by anything."

In other words, even Christians who have been set free by Jesus can allow things to master them and can return to being slaves of sin. Even good and wholesome things can master us, if we cross a line and start using them to fill the place in our lives which is meant to be filled by God.

As well as giving the enemy a foothold in our lives, compulsive behaviors can lead to physical and mental health problems.

> It is for freedom that Christ has set us free. Stand firm, then, and do not let yourselves be burdened again by a yoke of slavery (Galatians 5:1).

The first step towards freedom from addiction is to be honest enough to recognize that you have a problem in a particular area.

Pray the following prayer:

Father God,
Thank You that it is for freedom that Jesus set me free and that I no longer have to be a slave to sin.
I confess, however, that I have made wrong choices, and have allowed sin to master me. Please show me now all the areas where I am not walking in complete freedom, so that I can take hold of my freedom and stand firm.
In Jesus' name.
Amen.

Mark items on the list that you recognize have been an issue for you:

- ❑ Comfort eating / regularly eating unhealthy food
- ❑ Self-harm
- ❑ Abuse of substances (including prescription drugs, street drugs, alcohol, nicotine, laxatives, caffeine)
- ❑ Starving yourself / anorexia
- ❑ Running on adrenaline / not taking enough rest
- ❑ Gambling
- ❑ Pornography / watching TV programs or movies with sexual content
- ❑ Sex / masturbation
- ❑ Electronic devices / social media / online gaming
- ❑ Other: _____

Father,

I confess that I have deceived myself by thinking that I can indulge in sin without being mastered by it. I have allowed sin to master me in these areas of my life: _____.

I turn away from these sins and take back the ground that I have given to the enemy.

Thank You that You have given me free will and I can choose to say yes or no to anything. Thank You that I can take tempting thoughts captive and bring them to You.

Thank You that I am not defined by past addictions. I am a holy, loved, forgiven child of God despite my past sins. I am no longer a slave to sin.

In Jesus' name.

Amen.

Take a moment to try to work out the lies you have believed that have drawn you towards addictions (e.g., that I can drink as much alcohol as I like without any consequences; that food will bring me lasting comfort). Lasting change will come as you choose to renew your mind to the truth of God's Word.

Consider whether it would be helpful to make yourself accountable to someone as you move forward. Contact them *now* while the thought is fresh in your mind. Do you recognize that you need to seek medical or professional help? Again, take the first step *now*.

Step 8: The Temple Of The Holy Spirit

Or do you not know that your body is a temple of the Holy Spirit within you, whom you have from God? You are not your own, for you were bought with a price. So glorify God in your body. (1 Corinthians 6:19-20 ESV)

Your body is a temple of the Holy Spirit – a holy place – and you are a holy one. We glorify God in our bodies when we live according to who we are, when we choose to live by the Spirit and not by the flesh.

Father God,

Thank You for my physical body. Thank You for its amazing design and the way you knitted me together in my mother's womb. I really am "fearfully and wonderfully made" (Psalm 139:14).

Please show me now the ways in which I have not honored You in my body or have believed lies about it.

In Jesus' name.

Amen.

Consider the following list:
- ❏ Thinking that my value comes from the appearance or shape of my body.
- ❏ Thinking that my body is all-important rather than simply my temporary accommodation on earth.
- ❏ Thinking that how I treat my body is unimportant.
- ❏ Making an idol out of physical perfection or fitness.
- ❏ Not exercising my body regularly.
- ❏ Believing that having a weak or frail body prevents me from being used mightily by God or accomplishing everything that He has for me to do.
- ❏ Deliberately harming my body.
- ❏ Eating and drinking in a way that I know is likely to harm my body.
- ❏ Filling my life with activity and neglecting to rest.
- ❏ Other: _____

Pray the following prayer for each item you have marked:

> **Father God,**
>
> I confess that I have sinned by _____.
>
> **I recognize the truth that my body is the temple of the Holy Spirit and here and now I offer myself to You afresh as a living sacrifice. Thank You that I am holy and pleasing to You** (Romans 12:1).
>
> **In Jesus' name.**
>
> **Amen.**

What specific changes do you resolve to make in your diet, exercise, or rest patterns? Write them below and commit each one of them to God in prayer.

Step 9: Anxiety And Fear

Anxiety

> Humble yourselves, therefore, under the mighty hand of God so that at the proper time he may exalt you, casting all your anxieties on him, because he cares for you. (1 Peter 5:6-7 ESV)

How can we deal with anxiety? This passage gives you two things to do: humble yourself and cast all your anxieties on God.

1. Humbling Ourselves By Adopting God's Goal For Our Lives

Part of humbling ourselves under God's mighty hand is to do with letting go of our own agenda and adopting God's goal for our lives. Feeling continually anxious is a strong indication that you may be working towards a life-goal that feels uncertain, one whose fulfilment depends on people or circumstances that are not under your direct control.

> Father God,
> You are so much bigger than I can imagine. You know the end from the beginning. Your ways are perfect.
> I confess that I have tried to run my life myself rather than letting You do it. I have tried to control people and events that are beyond my ability to influence. As a result I have often felt anxious.
> I humbly ask You to show me where I have developed life-goals that do not align with Your goal for my life, to become more and more like Jesus in character.
> In Jesus' name.
> Amen.

A life-goal is a goal you have developed for your life that feels so important to you that you measure your whole success as a person against it. A wrong life-goal is one whose fulfilment depends on people or circumstances that you can't legitimately influence. It may be a worthy goal in its own right but if it has become an idol to us, it is a problem.

Mark unhealthy life-goals that you recognize in yourself:

- ☐ To live a long healthy life.
- ☐ To be physically fit.
- ☐ To be healed.
- ☐ To have a certain level of financial security.
- ☐ To have children or a spouse who serve God and live fruitful lives.
- ☐ To rise to a certain position in my career.
- ☐ Other: _____

Pray the following prayer for each wrong life-goal you have identified:

Lord God,

I confess that I have made these life-goals too important in my thinking [name them].

I recognize the truth that, whether or not they are achieved, means nothing in terms of my core identity or success as a person.

I know I can continue to work towards goals that are good in themselves, but I will no longer measure myself by whether or not they are fulfilled.

Instead I choose to adopt Your life-goal for me, which is to become more and more like Jesus in character.

In Jesus' name.

Amen.

2. Casting Anxiety Onto Jesus

Start this section by praying as follows:

> Lord God,
>
> You have commanded me in Your Word not to be anxious. I recognize, therefore, that it must be entirely possible for me to live without anxiety. I bring You the situations that are causing me anxiety and ask You to give me wisdom to separate facts from assumptions, and understand what my responsibility is in each situation.
>
> In this time of reflection, please help me see my present circumstances as they really are.
>
> Thank You that You have promised me that You will not let me be tested beyond what I can bear and that You are working in every situation for my good.
>
> In Jesus' name.
>
> Amen.

To begin with, simply make a list of all circumstances in your life that are difficult and are causing you ongoing anxiety:

Then take each situation you have listed one at a time:

1. Write down the basic facts about the situation, taking care not to make any assumptions beyond the basic facts. For example, a fact would be, "I have found a strange lump." A corresponding assumption would be, "I have cancer and I am going to die." List any false assumptions you recognize you have made:

2. Ask yourself: what in this situation do I have the right or responsibility to do something about? And what is beyond my legitimate ability to influence? Write down the things that you have a responsibility to do and do them. For example, if you have found a strange lump, your responsibilities might be to pray about it and make an appointment to see your doctor.

When you have done what is yours to do; then you can confidently leave the rest to God by praying as follows:

Lord God,

I bring to You the situation regarding _____.
Having fulfilled my responsibilities in this situation, I now cast my anxiety onto You.

I do not trust in myself or my own abilities to resolve it. I do not trust in other people to resolve it. I choose to trust in You alone and I confidently leave it in Your powerful hands.

In Jesus' name.

Amen.

Fear

Unhealthy fear is fear that is not a reasonable response to what is happening, e.g., being paralyzed by a small spider in the corner of the room, thinking we are going to get ill at any moment, or sleeping with the light on because of fear of the dark.

Most unhealthy fears are related to the fear of other people, or to the fear of death.

For a fear to be healthy it has to have two attributes: it has to be both *present* and *powerful*. Every unhealthy fear comes from believing that an object is both present and powerful when it is not. In other words, there is a lie behind every unhealthy fear.

Pray the following prayer:

Lord God,
Please show me where I have been fearful and help me work out the lie behind each fear.
In Jesus' name.
Amen.

Now mark the fears you recognize affect you:

- ❑ Fear of death
- ❑ Fear of other people (name them: _____)
- ❑ Fear of sickness
- ❑ Fear of disability
- ❑ Fear of having no money
- ❑ Fear of failure
- ❑ Fear of displeasing God
- ❑ Other:_____

For each fear you have marked, write down the lie that you have believed together with a corresponding truth from God's Word:

FEAR   **LIE**   **TRUTH**

For each unhealthy fear, pray the following prayer:

Father God,
Thank You that I no longer have to live with unhealthy fears.
I reject the unhealthy fear of _____. I have believed the lie that _____. Thank You for the truth that _____.
In Jesus' name.
Amen.

The Fear Of Physical Death

Hebrews 2:14-15 says that Christ died that, "by his death he might break the power of him who holds the power of death – that is, the devil – and free those who all their lives were held in slavery by their fear of death."

We can't remove the *presence* of death. Unless Jesus comes back first, the one thing in life we can be 100% sure of is that our physical body will die. But:

> Listen, I tell you a mystery: We will not all sleep, but we will all be changed – in a flash, in the twinkling of an eye, at the last trumpet. For the trumpet will sound, the dead will be raised imperishable, and we will be changed.
> (1 Corinthians 15:51-52)

Death is no longer *powerful*. It has "lost its sting" (1 Corinthians 15:54-57). The Bible promises that Heaven will be a place free from tears, pain, and mourning (Revelation 21: 3-4).

It is healthy to live in the light of the death of our physical body. The Apostle Paul did just that. Writing from prison in Rome with the likelihood of a death sentence coming his way he wrote this to the Philippians:

> It is my eager expectation and hope that I will not be at all ashamed, but that with full courage now as always Christ will be honored in my body, whether by life or by death. For to me to live is Christ, and to die is gain. If I am to live in the flesh, that means fruitful labor for me. Yet which I shall choose I cannot tell. I am hard pressed between the two. My desire is to depart and be with Christ, for that is far better. But to remain in the flesh is more necessary on your account.
> (Philippians 1:20-24 ESV)

Paul is torn between staying in the temporary tent of his body and leaving for the joys of heaven. But whether he lives or dies, he wants Christ to be honored in his body.

Read the following prayer through carefully once or twice. Then pray it through:

> Father God,
>
> I joyfully declare the truth that Jesus died to break the power of the devil, and to free me from the fear of death. I choose to live in that freedom.
>
> I reject and turn away from the fear of death.
>
> I declare the truth that, when my body dies, my spirit will live on with You. Death has lost its sting and no longer holds any power over me.
>
> I entrust myself completely to You. May You decide the timing and manner of my physical death. In the meantime I commit myself to fruitful labor in Your Kingdom in the power of Your Holy Spirit. Please use me to the fullest possible extent to do the works You have prepared in advance for me to do.
>
> For me, to live is Christ and to die is gain.
>
> Amen.

Step 10: Facing Chronic Illness

Please go through this Step if you have a chronic condition. If you do not, go straight to the Closing Prayer on page 175.

We know that nothing is impossible for God and that He can heal supernaturally. But there is an element of mystery about this, and if we are not healed it does not necessarily mean that we don't have enough faith or that there is some other thing wrong with us. God is interested in our wholeness – spirit, mind, and body – not just physical healing.

Having a chronic condition does not in any way prevent you being a whole, fruitful disciple. In fact it can help you towards becoming that as you persevere through the difficulties and limitations it brings and become more and more like Jesus in character.

Read through the following prayer carefully once or twice. Then, when you are ready, use it to entrust yourself completely to God:

Father,

Thank You that Jesus died and rose again so that I can be whole and fruitful. Thank You that Your divine power has already given me everything I need to live a godly life (2 Peter 1:3) and that my wholeness and fruitfulness do not depend in any way on being physically healed.

I present to You my whole being as a living sacrifice. Be glorified in me, Father. Do what You want to do in me and through me.

I put into Your hands the question of my physical healing. Please show me if there is anything more I need to do. Otherwise I simply wait for You and trust You. Your ways are far above my ways (Isaiah 55:8-9). You are good, loving, and powerful. I put my trust solely in You. I rejoice in You. I worship You with the whole of my being.

I forgive those who have implied that I have not been healed because I do not have enough faith or because there is some other thing wrong with me.

I thank You for Your words to Paul: "My grace is sufficient for you, for My power is made perfect in weakness" (2 Corinthians 12:9). Thank You that they are true of me too. Your grace is enough. Your power is made perfect in my weakness.

Please help me live within my physical limitations, but nevertheless please use me to the fullest possible extent as a disciple of Jesus.

In Jesus' name.

Amen.

Closing Prayer

Having submitted to God, we now need to resist the devil, and when we do, he has no choice but to *flee* from us (James 4:7) – not just to depart in an orderly fashion! Pray the following prayer:

> **Father God,**
>
> **Thank You for leading me in this process.**
>
> **Thank You for showing me my sin and reassuring me of Your forgiveness and love.**
>
> **Having submitted to You by confessing my sin, I now resist the devil as You command me** (James 4:7). **I tell every enemy of the Lord Jesus Christ to leave me.**
>
> **In Jesus' name.**
>
> **Amen.**

Conclude the process by asking God to fill you with His Holy Spirit and to continue to lead you into all truth.

Calling The Elders

> Is any one of you in trouble? He should pray. Is anyone happy? Let him sing songs of praise. Is any one of you sick? He should call the elders of the church to pray over him and anoint him with oil in the name of the Lord. And the prayer offered in faith will make the sick person well; the Lord will raise him up. If he has sinned, he will be forgiven. Therefore confess your sins to each other and pray for each other so that you may be healed. The prayer of a righteous man is powerful and effective. (James 5:13-16)

During this process you have been assuming your responsibility to pray and to confess sin. You have submitted to God and resisted the devil.

If you still have a health issue, it remains for you to ask the elders of your church to anoint you with oil and to pray for you as James instructs.
We would expect any issue with a spiritual root to disappear at that point. If the illness continues, it would be reasonable to assume that this is not an issue with a spiritual root.

If you are going through this process as part of a group in your church, your elders will now anoint you with oil and pray for your healing.

If you have been doing this on your own, explain to the elders of your church what you have done and ask them if they will now anoint you with oil and pray for your healing.

If you are not in a church, we would encourage you to join one.

Renewing Your Mind

We are transformed through the renewing of our minds. Before you finish the process, ask God to highlight for you where you need to change your belief system. What faulty beliefs has He helped you identify as you have gone through *The Steps To Healing And Wholeness*? Where do you need to do some work to renew your mind?

Pray the following prayer:

> **Heavenly Father,**
>
> **I commit myself to living according to the truth. Thank you for revealing to me ways in which I have not been doing that. I ask you now through the Spirit of Truth to show me the key strongholds in my mind, the areas where my belief system has been faulty. I commit myself to renewing my mind so that I will be transformed and will become the person and the leader you want me to be.**
>
> **In Jesus' name.**
>
> **Amen.**

Sit in silence and write down areas where you realize your thinking has been faulty (ie does not line up with what God says in His Word). Bear in mind that the faulty thinking will still *feel* true to you. It might help to look back through the Steps and the notes you have made during the course. Consider especially the section when you forgave other people and told God how the things that were done to you made you feel. What were the words you used? Repeated occurrences of the same word – "inadequate", "inferior", "hopeless", or whatever – may well indicate a stronghold. None of those things is true for a child of God.

Then pick no more than three key faulty beliefs that you will commit to focus on to renew your mind and write them on pages 196-198. On the left-hand side write down the faulty belief and on the right side write what God says in His Word. Write as many verses as you can find that say what is really true.

For the first area, write a Stronghold-Buster (see the notes on page 53):

I refuse to believe the lie that...

I speak out the truth that [list the truth from the verses you found].

Declare it every day for the next 40 days or until you know that your belief system has changed. You could use pages 62-67 to create your Stronghold-Buster.

When you have successfully been through a Stronghold-Buster for the first faulty belief, come back and do the same for the second one, and then the third one.

Imagine how much more fruitful you would be as a disciple of Jesus if you could deal completely with these issues. And you can!

Any Questions?

WHAT'S IT ABOUT?

This session was not in the original plan but was an idea that arose during the filming of the main sessions. Members of the studio audience were invited to submit questions that had arisen as they went through the course and, in this impromptu session, Steve, Ifeoma, and Mary do their best to answer them. It's a great way to round off the course!

OBJECTIVE:

To address any questions that may remain.

WELCOME

Back in the first session, we asked you, "If you were given the opportunity to ask God one question about health, wholeness, and fruitfulness as a disciple of Jesus, what would you ask Him?" Now that you have been through the course, we'd like you to consider that again. What are the questions that remain in your mind?

WORSHIP

Focus on God's amazing wisdom:

> I make known the end from the beginning, from ancient times, what is still to come. I say, "My purpose will stand, and I will do all that I please." (Isaiah 46:10)

> "For my thoughts are not your thoughts, neither are your ways my ways," declares the Lord. "As the heavens are higher than the earth, so are my ways higher than your ways and my thoughts than your thoughts." (Isaiah 55:8-9)

> For the foolishness of God is wiser than human wisdom, and the weakness of God is stronger than human strength. (1 Corinthians 1:25)

Video length: 46:36

WORD

Question Time!

The questions raised by the studio audience are listed below in the order in which they occur with space for you to add your notes. As you watch the video, you might like to pause it after each question has been answered to add your own thoughts or to discuss together what has been said.

I have done everything I know to do, but ailments like high blood pressure and diabetes won't shift. What can I do?

When we visit the doctor and get a diagnosis for our symptoms but don't then get a cure, we still have a label. How can we live with that?

Why does God heal some people and not others?

What is the point of the menopause?

What would you suggest if someone has done a Stronghold-Buster many times and still hasn't seen breakthrough?

Death itself is not such a frightening prospect to me. I have a condition that means, unless the Lord heals me, that I will suffer in the process of dying. That does bring fear to me. How do we approach this?

Why does God allow suffering?

Why is the Church largely silent on the dangers of unhealthy eating and unhealthy lifestyles?

God told Paul he would have to live with his thorn in the flesh (2 Corinthians 12:7-9). How do you know when a particular ailment is like Paul's thorn in the flesh?

How can we know if a particular alternative therapy is OK?

Note: the book mentioned during the answer to this question is *The Biblical Guide To Alternative Medicine* by Neil T. Anderson and Michael Jacobson (Regal Books, 2003).

Jesus said "It is your faith that made you well." What role does faith play in healing?

Why is it that, when Christians work for Jesus, they come under Satanic attack?

If you have time, you might like to discuss together possible answers to other questions raised during the Welcome section or any other questions that occur to participants. Don't worry if you don't arrive at a satisfactory answer. Remember:

If any of you lacks wisdom, you should ask God, who gives generously to all without finding fault, and it will be given to you. (James 1:5)

FREEDOM
IN CHRIST

Impact Your Community And Grow Your Church

Can We Help You Make Fruitful Disciples?

A church with growing, fruitful disciples of Jesus is a growing, fruitful church that is making a real difference in the community where God has placed it. A key question for church leaders is: "How can I help our people become mature, fruitful disciples as quickly as possible so that they go out and make a real impact?"

A fundamental part of the answer is to help them understand the principles that underlie all of Freedom In Christ's discipleship resources for churches:

- **TRUTH** Know who you are in Christ.
- **TURNING** Ruthlessly close any doors you've opened to the enemy through past sin and don't open any more.
- **TRANSFORMATION** Renew your mind to the truth of God's Word (which is how you will be transformed).

Freedom In Christ has equipped hundreds of thousands of church leaders around the world to use this "identity-based discipleship" approach. As churches base their discipleship around these principles, they report not only changed individual lives but whole changed churches. When churches start to look less like hospitals, full of those who are constantly struggling with their own issues, and more like part of the Bride of Christ, they make an increasing impact on their community.

Our mission is to equip the Church to transform the nations by providing church leaders with transformational discipleship resources that can be used right across their church. Some are specially tailored to the communication styles of different groups such as young people and millennials. Others build on our main Freedom In Christ Course. You can see some of them on the following pages.

Our heart is to help church leaders develop a long-term, whole-church discipleship strategy. Our offices and Representatives around the world run training courses and have people on the ground who like nothing better than to discuss discipleship with church leaders. If you think we can help you in any way as you look to make fruitful disciples, please get in touch.

Find your local office at: www.FreedomInChrist.org

The Freedom In Christ Course

Now in its third edition and translated into well over 30 languages, *The Freedom In Christ Course* can transform the way you help Christians become fruitful disciples. Focused on firstly establishing every Christian in the sure foundation of their identity in Jesus, it gives them the tools to break free and stay free from all that holds them back, and a strategy for ongoing transformation. It has ten teaching sessions presented by Steve Goss, Nancy Maldonado, and Daryl Fitzgerald plus *The Steps To Freedom In Christ* ministry component presented by Steve Goss and Neil Anderson.

With a specially designed app, extra teaching films, a worship album, Leader's Guide, Participant's Guide, and tons of extras, *The Freedom In Christ Course* offers you everything you need to make disciples who bear fruit that will last!

"Men, women, and middle and high school students have been radically transformed."

Bob Huisman, Pastor, Immanuel Christian Reformed Church, Hudsonville, MI, USA

"I recommend it highly to anyone serious about discipleship."

Chuah Seong Peng, Senior Pastor, Holy Light Presbyterian Church, Johor Baru, Malaysia

"The *Freedom In Christ Course* changed me and put me in a position to minister to people in a much more effective way."

Frikkie Elstadt, Every Nation Patria, Mossel Bay, South Africa

"Our church has changed as a result of this course. Those who come to Christ and who do the course end up with a rock solid start to their faith."

Pastor Sam Scott, Eltham Baptist Church, Australia

disciple – FIC's Message For The Millennial Generation

Church leaders report that discipling those in their 20s and 30s is one of their biggest challenges. disciple is a powerful tool to help you. It speaks the language of 20s and 30s and invites them to dive into the greatest story ever told, God's story. They will learn how to take hold of their freedom and discover their mandate.

- 10 sessions designed to run for approximately 90 minutes each.
- Impactful Starter Films introduce the theme for each session.
- Extra films (via the app) on topics including sex, the occult, and fear.
- Chat and Reflect times allow teaching to take root.
- App with extra teaching films, daily devotional, daily nuggets of extra teaching, and Stronghold–Buster–Builder with reminders.

"Thank you so much for caring enough to do this. You have no idea how much it means to us that you have taken the time to understand and help us overcome all the stuff that comes at us."

"You really get us and understand us, you don't patronize us and talk down to us."

"God is doing incredible things in the young people at our church and I'm just grateful this course has been able to facilitate that."

"*disciple* is really user-friendly. The young adults really engaged and there were definite light bulb moments."

Freedom In Christ For Young People

The aim of *Freedom in Christ for Young People* is to set young people firmly on the way to becoming fruitful disciples who are sold out for God and will make a radical difference. Watch them change as they connect with the truth about who they are in Christ, become free from pressures that hold them back, and learn to renew their thinking.

The emphasis is on relevant, interactive, multi-media based material tailored to meet the needs of 11-18-year-olds. It is split into two age ranges, 11-14 and 15-18. Each session is packed full of age-appropriate games, activities, discussion-starters, film clip suggestions and talk slots.

"Every young disciple is looking to engage with Jesus in a way that will change lives. This innovative, exciting course will help young people discover the truth of who they are in Christ and be set free to be all that God has made them as a result."

Mike Pilavachi, Founder of Soul Survivor

"Freedom in Christ is a creative and relevant course for teenagers with the potential to produce a generation of fruitful young disciples."

Martin Saunders, Editor of Youthwork Magazine

The Lightbringers For Children

The Lightbringers is a powerful resource for churches and parents to use with 5-to-11-year-olds. It is designed to equip them to become fruitful disciples who stay connected to Jesus into their adult lives. They will understand:

*   Who they are in Jesus;
*   What they have in Jesus;
*   How to become fruitful disciples who follow Jesus closely.

It consists of ten action-packed sessions plus specially-written versions of *The Steps To Freedom In Christ* ministry component and has versions for two age groups (5-8 and 9-11). It's great for churches, Bible clubs, and families.

The **Church Edition** includes a comprehensive 276-page Leader's Guide plus downloadable videos, songs, activity sheets, and PowerPoint presentations. The **Family Edition** is an online-only version designed to be delivered in the home.

"Parents, educators, children's leaders, and pastors rejoice! There is no longer a void in quality children's curriculum that instills the essentials of identity in Christ and freedom in Christ."

"*The Lightbringers* is a fantastic resource to help children know their identity in Christ and how to view the rest of the world through that lens."

"It has awesome content, is easy to follow, and will fill what has been a huge gap in kids' ministry up to this time."

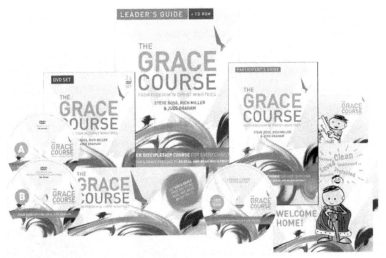

The Grace Course

If you don't first know God's love for you in your *heart* – not just your *head* – it's impossible for your life to be motivated by love for Him. Instead you are likely to end up motivated more by guilt or shame or fear or pride. You may be doing all the "right" things, believing all the right things and saying all the right things, but there will be precious little fruit.

- Six sessions plus *The Steps to Experiencing God's Grace*.
- Present it yourself or use the video presentations.
- Video testimonies illustrating the teaching points, practical exercises, times of listening to God, and Pause For Thought times.
- Works especially well as a course during Lent.

"For the first time in the decades that I've been a Christian, I'm suddenly 'getting' grace – it's amazing and it's shocking!"

"I realized that it's not about my performance – He just wants my heart."

"It was AMAZING! During the last session after we had finished nobody moved for what seemed like ages. When the silence eventually did break, people began to spontaneously share all that the course had meant to them. Testimonies to what the Lord had done just flowed out, some were life-changing."

"*The Grace Course* does a marvelous job in introducing the concept of grace in a simple, engaging and, at times, even humorous way. It is short and to the point, taking an incredibly deep theological issue and making it understandable and practical."

Freed To Lead

Freed To Lead is a 10-week discipleship course for Christians who are called to leadership – whether in the marketplace, public service, the Church or any other context. It will transform your leadership, free you from drivenness and burnout, enable you to survive personal attacks, use conflict positively, and overcome other barriers to effective leadership.

- Ten sessions plus *Steps to Freedom for Leaders*
- Video testimonies and Pause For Thought discussion times
- Ideal for church leadership teams before rolling out across the church

"The Freed To Lead course has been the most amazing leadership development experience of my career, having been called to both marketplace and church leadership for over 20 years. It dispels worldly leadership myths and practices and provides Biblical foundations for Godly leadership. I wholeheartedly recommend this course for anyone who aspires or is currently called to Godly servant-hearted leadership in any arena."

"An outstanding course – inspirational and motivational, affirming and encouraging."

"It has reinforced my conviction that my identity is first and foremost in Christ, whatever leadership role I may hold."

FREEDOM**STREAM**
On-Demand Videos For Our Courses

You can access all of our video material for small group studies online for one low monthly subscription. Try it for free!

Access to all the main Freedom In Christ small group courses so you can browse or use the entire range including:

> The *Freedom In Christ Course*;
> The *Lightbringers – Freedom In Christ For Children*;
> *Freedom In Christ For Young People*;
> *disciple* (the Freedom In Christ message for 18s to 30s);
> The *Grace Course*;
> *Freed To Lead*;
> *Keys To Health, Wholeness, & Fruitfulness*.

Free video training courses for course leaders and their teams:

> *Making Fruitful Disciples* – the Biblical principles of discipleship;
> *Helping Others Find Freedom In Christ*.

- No need to buy several DVD sets if you have multiple groups running.
- Access is for all members of your church so participants can catch up if they miss a session.

For further information, pricing, and to start your free trial go to:
FreedomInChrist.org/FreedomStream

Get In Touch

Freedom In Christ exists to equip the Church to make fruitful disciples who make a real impact in their community. Our passion is to help church leaders develop a discipleship strategy right across their church that will be effective for years to come. How can we help your church?

We offer:
* A series of introductory and training events for church leaders;
* Advice on establishing a discipleship strategy for your church built around our discipleship resources;
* Training and equipping for those in your church who will be involved in implementing that strategy.

For contact details of Freedom In Christ in your country or to find out how to order our resources, go to:

FreedomInChrist.org

Join Us!

If, like us, you are excited about seeing this message of "Truth, Turning, and Transformation" spread throughout the Church around the world, please join us.

Join our team of international supporters
Freedom In Christ exists to equip the Church worldwide to make fruitful disciples. We rely heavily for financial support from people who have understood how important it is to give leaders the tools that will enable them to help people become fruitful *disciples*, not just *converts*, especially when we are opening up an office in a new country. Typically your support will be used to:

- create new resources such as this one;
- help establish new Freedom In Christ offices around the world;
- translate our resources into other languages;
- partner with other organizations worldwide to equip leaders;
- equip church leaders around the world.

Join the team of supporters in your country
We are passionate about working with those who have themselves been touched by the Biblical message of freedom. Financial support enables us to develop new resources and get them into the hands of more church leaders. As a result, many, many people are connecting with this life-changing message. There are always new projects – small and large – that don't happen unless there's funding.

To find out more please go to: **FreedomInChrist.org/friends**

Faulty Thinking (Lies)	What God Says (Truth)

Faulty Thinking (Lies)　　## What God Says (Truth)

Faulty Thinking (Lies)	What God Says (Truth)

CPSIA information can be obtained
at www.ICGtesting.com
Printed in the USA
LVHW010640060919
630114LV00002B/3